WAVES

UNIVERSITY MATHEMATICAL TEXTS

GENERAL EDITORS

ALEXANDER C. AITKEN, D.Sc., F.R.S.

DANIEL E. RUTHERFORD, D.Sc., Dr. Math.

WAVES

A MATHEMATICAL ACCOUNT OF THE
COMMON TYPES OF WAVE MOTION

BY

C. A. COULSON, M.A., D.Sc., F.R.S.

ROUSE BALL PROFESSOR OF APPLIED
MATHEMATICS, OXFORD

With 30 Figures

OLIVER AND BOYD
EDINBURGH AND LONDON
NEW YORK : INTERSCIENCE PUBLISHERS, INC.

First Edition	•	•	•	1941
Second Edition	•	•	•	1943
Third Edition	•	•	•	1944
Fourth Edition	•	•	•	1947
Fifth Edition	•	•	•	1949
Sixth Edition	•	•	•	1952
Seventh Edition	•	•	•	**1955**

PRINTED AND PUBLISHED IN GREAT BRITAIN BY
OLIVER AND BOYD LTD., EDINBURGH

PREFACE

THE object of this book is to consider from an elementary standpoint as many different types of wave motion as possible. In almost every case the fundamental problem is the same, since it consists in solving the standard equation of wave motion ; the various applications differ chiefly in the conditions imposed upon these solutions. For this reason it is desirable that the subject of waves should be treated as one whole, rather than in several distinct parts ; the present tendency is in this direction.

It is presupposed that the reader is familiar with the elements of vector analysis, the simpler results of which are freely quoted. In a sense this present volume may be regarded as a sequel to Rutherford's *Vector Methods*, published in this series.

In a volume of this size, it is not possible to deal thoroughly with any one branch of the subject : nor indeed is this desirable in a book which is intended as an introduction to the more specialised and elaborate treatises necessary to the specialist. This book is intended for University students covering a general course of Applied Mathematics or Natural Philosophy in the final year of their honours degree. A few topics, such as elastic waves in continuous media, or at the common boundary of two media, and radiation from aerials, have unavoidably had to be omitted for lack of space. The reader is referred to any of the standard works on elasticity and wireless for a discussion of these problems.

This book would not be complete without a reference of gratitude to my friends Dr D. E. Rutherford and Prof. G. S. Rushbrooke, who have read the proofs, checked most of the examples and contributed in no small way to the clarity of my arguments. My thanks are also offered to my wife for her share in the preparation of the manuscript.

C. A. C.

January 1941.

PREFACE TO SEVENTH EDITION

I should like to thank several friends for pointing out certain misprints in the earlier editions, and for making suggestions that have led to a clearer presentation of the argument in one or two places.

C. A. C.

May 1955.

CONTENTS

ix

CHAPTER VI

SOUND WAVES

CHAPTER VII

ELECTRIC WAVES

CHAPTER VIII

GENERAL CONSIDERATIONS

CHAPTER I

THE EQUATION OF WAVE MOTION

§ **1.** We are all familiar with the idea of a wave; thus, when a pebble is dropped into a pond, water waves travel radially outwards; when a piano is played, the wires vibrate and sound waves spread through the room; when a wireless station is transmitting, electric waves move through the ether. These are all examples of wave motion, and they have two important properties in common: firstly, energy is propagated to distant points; and secondly, the disturbance travels through the medium without giving the medium as a whole any permanent displacement. Thus the ripples spread outwards over a pond carrying energy with them, but as we can see by watching the motion of a small floating body, the water of the pond itself does not move with the waves. In the following chapters we shall find that whatever the nature of the medium which transmits the waves, whether it be air, a stretched string, a liquid, an electric cable or the ether, these two properties which are common to all these types of wave motion, will enable us to relate them together. They are all governed by a certain differential equation, the Equation of Wave Motion (see § 5), and the mathematical part of each separate problem merely consists in solving this equation with the right boundary conditions, and then interpreting the solution appropriately.

§ **2.** Consider a disturbance ϕ which is propagated along the x axis with velocity c. There is no need to

1   **A**

state explicitly what ϕ refers to ; it may be the elevation of a water wave or the magnitude of a fluctuating electric field. Then, since the disturbance is moving, ϕ will depend on x and t. When $t = 0$, ϕ will be some function of x which we may call $f(x)$. $f(x)$ is the **wave profile**, since if we plot the disturbance ϕ against x, and " photograph " the wave at $t = 0$, the curve obtained will be $\phi = f(x)$. If we suppose that the wave is propagated without change of shape, then a photograph taken at a later time t will be identical with that at $t = 0$, except that the wave profile has moved a distance ct in the positive direction of the x axis. If we took a new origin at the point $x = ct$, and let distances measured from this origin be called X, so that $x = X + ct$, then the equation of the wave profile referred to this new origin would be

$$\phi = f(X).$$

Referred to the original fixed origin, this means that

$$\phi = f(x - ct) \qquad . \qquad . \qquad . \qquad . \qquad (1)$$

This equation is the most general expression of a wave moving with constant velocity c and without change of shape, along the positive direction of x. If the wave is travelling in the negative direction its form is given by (1) with the sign of c changed, i.e.

$$\phi = f(x + ct) . \qquad . \qquad . \qquad . \qquad . \qquad (2)$$

§ 3. The simplest example of a wave of this kind is the **harmonic wave,** in which the wave profile is a sine or cosine curve. Thus if the wave profile at $t = 0$ is

$$(\phi)_{t=0} = a \cos mx,$$

then at time t, the displacement, or disturbance, is

$$\phi = a \cos m(x - ct) \qquad . \qquad . \qquad . \qquad (3)$$

The maximum value of the disturbance, viz. a, is called the **amplitude.** The wave profile repeats itself at regular distances $2\pi/m$. This is known as the **wavelength** λ. Equation (3) could therefore be written

$$\phi = a \cos \frac{2\pi}{\lambda}(x-ct) \quad . \quad . \quad . \quad . \quad (4)$$

The time taken for one complete wave to pass any point is called the **period** τ of the wave. It follows from (4) that $\frac{2\pi}{\lambda}(x-ct)$ must pass through a complete cycle of values as t is increased by τ. Thus

$$\frac{2\pi c\tau}{\lambda} = 2\pi,$$

i.e.
$$\tau = \lambda/c \quad . \quad . \quad . \quad . \quad (5)$$

The **frequency** n of the wave is the number of waves passing a fixed observer in unit time. Clearly

$$n = 1/\tau \quad . \quad . \quad . \quad . \quad (6)$$

so that
$$c = n\lambda, \quad . \quad . \quad . \quad . \quad (7)$$

and equation (4) may be written in either of the equivalent forms,

$$\phi = a \cos 2\pi\left(\frac{x}{\lambda} - \frac{t}{\tau}\right) \quad . \quad . \quad . \quad (8)$$

$$\phi = a \cos 2\pi\left(\frac{x}{\lambda} - nt\right) \quad . \quad . \quad . \quad (9)$$

Sometimes it is useful to introduce the **wave number** k, which is the number of waves in unit distance. Then

$$k = 1/\lambda, \quad . \quad . \quad . \quad . \quad (10)$$

and we may write equation (9)

$$\phi = a \cos 2\pi(kx-nt) \quad . \quad . \quad . \quad (11)$$

If we compare two similar waves

$$\phi_1 = a \cos 2\pi(kx - nt),$$
$$\phi_2 = a \cos\{2\pi(kx - nt) + \epsilon\},$$

we see that ϕ_2 is the same as ϕ_1 except that it is displaced a distance $\epsilon/2\pi k$, i.e. $\epsilon\lambda/2\pi$. ϵ is called the **phase** of ϕ_2 relative to ϕ_1. If $\epsilon = 2\pi, 4\pi, \ldots$ then the displacement is exactly one, two, $\ldots$ wavelengths, and we say that the waves are *in phase*; if $\epsilon = \pi, 3\pi, \ldots$ then the two waves are exactly *out of phase*.

Even if a wave is not a harmonic wave, but the wave profile consists of a regularly repeating pattern, the definitions of wavelength, period, frequency and wave number still apply, and equations (5), (6), (7) and (10) are still valid.

§ **4.** It is possible to generalise equation (1) to deal with the case of plane waves in three dimensions. A **plane wave** is one in which the disturbance is constant over all points of a plane drawn perpendicular to the direction of propagation. Such a plane is called a **wavefront**, and the wavefront moves perpendicular to itself with the velocity of propagation c. If the direction of propagation is $x : y : z = l : m : n$, where l, m, n are the direction cosines of the normal to each wavefront, then the equation of the wavefronts is

$$lx + my + nz = \text{const.,} \qquad \underleftarrow{r}. \qquad (12)$$

and at any moment t, ϕ is to be constant for all x, y, z satisfying (12). It is clear that

$$\phi = f(lx + my + nz - ct) \qquad . \qquad . \qquad (13)$$

is a function which fulfils all these requirements and therefore represents a plane wave travelling with velocity c in the direction $l : m : n$ without change of form.

§ **5.** The expression (13) is a particular solution of the equation of wave motion referred to on p. 1. Since l, m, n are direction cosines, $l^2 + m^2 + n^2 = 1$, and it is easily verified that ϕ satisfies the differential equation *

$$\nabla^2\phi \equiv \frac{\partial^2\phi}{\partial x^2} + \frac{\partial^2\phi}{\partial y^2} + \frac{\partial^2\phi}{\partial z^2} = \frac{1}{c^2}\frac{\partial^2\phi}{\partial t^2} \qquad (14)$$

This is the **equation of wave motion.**† It is one of the most important differential equations in the whole of mathematics, since it represents all types of wave motion in which the velocity is constant. The expressions in (1), (2), (8), **(9), (11)** and (13) are all particular solutions of this equation. We shall find, as we investigate different types of wave motion in subsequent chapters, that equation (14) invariably appears, and it will be our task to select the solution that is appropriate to our particular problem. There are certain types of solution that occur often, and we shall discuss some of them in the rest of this chapter, but before doing so, there is one important property of the fundamental equation that must be explained.

§ **6.** The equation of wave motion is *linear*. That is to say, ϕ and its differential coefficients never occur in any form other than that of the first degree. Consequently, if ϕ_1 and ϕ_2 are any two solutions of (14), $a_1\phi_1 + a_2\phi_2$ is also a solution, a_1 and a_2 being two arbitrary constants. This is an illustration of the **principle of superposition**, which states that, when all the relevant equations are linear, we may superpose any number of individual solutions to form new functions which are themselves also solutions. We shall often have occasion to do this.

A particular instance of this superposition, which is

---

* This equation has a close resemblance to Laplace's Equation which is discussed in Rutherford, *Vector Methods*, Chapter VII. The references, here and later, to this book refer to the first edition.

† Sometimes called the *wave equation*, but we do not use this phrase to avoid confusion with modern wave mechanics.

important in many problems, comes by adding together two harmonic waves going in different directions with the same amplitude and velocity. Thus, with two waves similar to (11) in opposite directions, we obtain

$$\phi = a \cos 2\pi(kx-nt) + a \cos 2\pi(kx+nt)$$
$$= 2a \cos 2\pi kx \cos 2\pi nt \quad . \quad . \quad . \quad . \quad (15)$$

This is known as a **stationary wave,** to distinguish it from the earlier **progressive waves.** It owes its name to the fact that the wave profile does not move forward. In fact, ϕ always vanishes at the points for which $\cos 2\pi kx = 0$, viz. $x = \pm\dfrac{1}{4k}, \pm\dfrac{3}{4k}, \pm\dfrac{5}{4k}, \ldots$. These points are called the **nodes,** and the intermediate points, where the amplitude of ϕ (i.e. $2a \cos 2\pi kx$) is greatest, are called **antinodes.** The distance between successive nodes, or successive antinodes, is $1/2k$, which, by (10), is half a wavelength.

Using harmonic wave functions similar to (13), we find stationary waves in three dimensions, given by

$$\phi = a \cos \frac{2\pi}{\lambda}(lx+my+nz-ct) + a \cos \frac{2\pi}{\lambda}(lx+my+nz+ct)$$

$$= 2a \cos \frac{2\pi}{\lambda}(lx+my+nz) \cos \frac{2\pi}{\lambda}ct \quad . \quad . \quad . \quad (16)$$

In this case ϕ always vanishes on the planes $lx+my+nz = \pm\dfrac{\lambda}{4}, \pm\dfrac{3\lambda}{4}, \ldots$, and these are known as **nodal planes.**

§ 7. We shall now obtain some special types of solution of the equation of wave motion ; we shall then be able to apply them to specific problems in later chapters. We may divide our solutions into two main types, representing stationary and progressive waves.

We have already dealt with progressive waves in one dimension. The equation to be solved is

$$\frac{\partial^2\phi}{\partial x^2} = \frac{1}{c^2} \frac{\partial^2\phi}{\partial t^2}.$$

Its most general solution may be obtained by a method due to D'Alembert. We change to new variables $u = x - ct$, and $v = x + ct$. Then it is easily verified that $\dfrac{\partial \phi}{\partial x}$ transforms to $\dfrac{\partial \phi}{\partial u} + \dfrac{\partial \phi}{\partial v}$, $\dfrac{\partial \phi}{\partial t}$ transforms to $-c\dfrac{\partial \phi}{\partial u} + c\dfrac{\partial \phi}{\partial v}$; $\dfrac{\partial^2 \phi}{\partial x^2}$ becomes $\dfrac{\partial^2 \phi}{\partial u^2} + 2\dfrac{\partial^2 \phi}{\partial u \partial v} + \dfrac{\partial^2 \phi}{\partial v^2}$, and finally $\dfrac{\partial^2 \phi}{\partial t^2}$ becomes $c^2 \left\{ \dfrac{\partial^2 \phi}{\partial u^2} - 2\dfrac{\partial^2 \phi}{\partial u \partial v} + \dfrac{\partial^2 \phi}{\partial v^2} \right\}$. When these changes are made the equation becomes $\dfrac{\partial^2 \phi}{\partial u \partial v} = 0$; the most general solution of this is

$$\phi = f(u) + g(v),$$

f and g being arbitrary functions. In the original variables this is

$$\phi = f(x - ct) + g(x + ct) \quad . \quad . \quad . \quad (17)$$

The harmonic waves of § 2 are special cases of this, in which f and g are cosine functions. The waves f and g travel with velocity c, in opposite directions.

In two dimensions the equation of wave motion is

$$\frac{\partial^2 \phi}{\partial x^2} + \frac{\partial^2 \phi}{\partial y^2} = \frac{1}{c^2}\frac{\partial^2 \phi}{\partial t^2} \quad . \quad . \quad . \quad (18)$$

By a method similar to D'Alembert's, it can be shown that the most general solution involving only plane * waves is

$$\phi = f(lx + my - ct) + g(lx + my + ct), \quad . \quad (19)$$

where, as before, f and g are arbitrary functions and $l^2 + m^2 = 1$.

In three dimensions the differential equation is

$$\frac{\partial^2 \phi}{\partial x^2} + \frac{\partial^2 \phi}{\partial y^2} + \frac{\partial^2 \phi}{\partial z^2} = \frac{1}{c^2}\frac{\partial^2 \phi}{\partial t^2} \quad . \quad . \quad (20)$$

and the most general solution involving only plane waves is

$$\phi = f(lx + my + nz - ct) + g(lx + my + nz + ct) \quad . \quad (21)$$

in which $l^2 + m^2 + n^2 = 1$.

---

* Strictly these should be called line waves, since at any moment ϕ is constant along the lines $lx + my = $ const.

There are, however, other solutions of progressive type, not involving plane waves. For suppose that we transform (20) to spherical polar coordinates r, θ, ψ.* The equation of wave motion becomes

$$\frac{\partial^2 \phi}{\partial r^2} + \frac{2}{r} \frac{\partial \phi}{\partial r} + \frac{1}{r^2 \sin \theta} \frac{\partial}{\partial \theta} \left(\sin \theta \frac{\partial \phi}{\partial \theta} \right) + \frac{1}{r^2 \sin^2 \theta} \frac{\partial^2 \phi}{\partial \psi^2} = \frac{1}{c^2} \frac{\partial^2 \phi}{\partial t^2}. \tag{22}$$

If we are interested in solutions possessing spherical symmetry (i.e. independent of θ and ψ) we shall have to solve the simpler equation

$$\frac{\partial^2 \phi}{\partial r^2} + \frac{2}{r} \frac{\partial \phi}{\partial r} = \frac{1}{c^2} \frac{\partial^2 \phi}{\partial t^2} \qquad \bullet \qquad \bullet \tag{23}$$

This may be written

$$\frac{\partial^2}{\partial r^2} (r\phi) = \frac{1}{c^2} \frac{\partial^2}{\partial t^2} (r\phi),$$

showing (cf. eq. (17)) that it has solutions

$$r\phi = f(r - ct) + g(r + ct),$$

f and g again being arbitrary functions. We see, therefore, that there are progressive type solutions

$$\phi = \frac{1}{r} f(r - ct) + \frac{1}{r} g(r + ct) \qquad . \qquad . \tag{24}$$

Let us now turn to solutions of stationary type. These may all be obtained by the method known as the separation of variables. In one dimension we have to solve

$$\frac{\partial^2 \phi}{\partial x^2} = \frac{1}{c^2} \frac{\partial^2 \phi}{\partial t^2}.$$

Let us try to find a solution of the form

$$\phi = X(x)T(t),$$

* See e.g. Rutherford, p. 62, equation **20**.

X and T being functions of x and t respectively, whose form is still to be discovered. Substituting this value of ϕ in the differential equation and dividing both sides by $X(x)T(t)$ we obtain

$$\frac{1}{X}\frac{d^2X}{dx^2} = \frac{1}{c^2T}\frac{d^2T}{dt^2} \qquad . \quad . \quad . \quad (25)$$

The left-hand side is independent of t, being only a function of x, and the right-hand side is independent of x. Since the two sides are identically equal, this implies that each is independent both of x and t, and must therefore be constant. Putting this constant equal to $-p^2$, we find

$$X'' + p^2X = 0, \ T'' + c^2p^2T = 0. \qquad . \quad . \quad (26)$$

These equations give, apart from arbitrary constants

$$X = \frac{\cos}{\sin}px \ , \ T = \frac{\cos}{\sin}cpt^* \quad . \quad . \quad (27)$$

A typical solution therefore is $a \cos px \cos cpt$, in which p is arbitrary. In this expression we could replace either or both of the cosines by sines, and by the principle of superposition the complete solution is the sum of any number of terms of this kind with different values of p.

The constant $-p^2$ which we introduced, is known as the **separation constant.** We were able to introduce it in (25) because the variables x and t had been completely separated from each other and were in fact on opposite sides of the equation. There was no reason why the separation constant should have had a negative value of $-p^2$ except that this enabled us to obtain harmonic solutions (27). If we had put each side of (25) equal to $+p^2$, the solutions would have been

$$X = e^{\pm px} \ , \ T = e^{\pm cpt} \qquad . \quad . \quad . \quad (28)$$

and our complete solution should therefore include terms of both types (27) and (28). The same distinction between the harmonic and exponential types of solution will occur frequently.

* This is read: X equals cos or sin px, etc.

This method of separation of variables can be extended to any number of dimensions. Thus in two dimensions a typical solution of (18) is

$$\phi = {\cos \atop \sin} px \, {\cos \atop \sin} qy \, {\cos \atop \sin} rct , \qquad . \qquad . \quad (29)$$

in which $p^2 + q^2 = r^2$, p and q being allowed arbitrary values. An alternative version of (29), in which one of the functions is exponential, is

$$\phi = {\cos \atop \sin} px \, e^{\pm qy} \, {\cos \atop \sin} rct. \qquad . \qquad . \quad (30)$$

in which $p^2 - q^2 = r^2$.

It is easy to see that there is a variety of forms similar to (30) in which one or more of the functions is altered from a harmonic to a hyperbolic or exponential term.

In three dimensions we have solutions of the same type, two typical examples being

$$\phi = {\cos \atop \sin} px \, {\cos \atop \sin} qy \, {\cos \atop \sin} rz \, {\cos \atop \sin} sct , \qquad p^2 + q^2 + r^2 = s^2 \quad (31)$$

$$\phi = {\cosh \atop \sinh} px \, e^{\pm qy} \, {\cos \atop \sin} rz \, {\cos \atop \sin} sct , \qquad -p^2 - q^2 + r^2 = s^2 \quad (32)$$

There are two other examples of solution in three dimensions that we shall discuss. In the first case we put $x = r \cos \theta$, $y = r \sin \theta$, and we use r, θ and z as cylindrical coordinates. The equation of wave motion becomes *

$$\frac{\partial^2 \phi}{\partial r^2} + \frac{1}{r} \frac{\partial \phi}{\partial r} + \frac{1}{r^2} \frac{\partial^2 \phi}{\partial \theta^2} + \frac{\partial^2 \phi}{\partial z^2} = \frac{1}{c^2} \frac{\partial^2 \phi}{\partial t^2}.$$

A solution can be found of the form

$$\phi = R(r)\Theta(\theta)Z(z)T(t), \qquad . \qquad . \qquad . \quad (33)$$

* See Rutherford, p. 63.

where, by the method of separation of variables, R, Θ, Z, T satisfy the equations

$$\frac{d^2R}{dr^2} + \frac{1}{r}\frac{dR}{dr} - \frac{m^2}{r^2}R + n^2R = 0,$$

$$\frac{d^2\Theta}{d\theta^2} = -m^2\Theta,$$

$$\frac{d^2Z}{dz^2} = -q^2Z,$$

$$\frac{d^2T}{dt^2} = -c^2p^2T , \quad n^2 = p^2 - q^2 \quad . \quad . \quad (34)$$

The only difficult equation is the first, and this * is just Bessel's equation of order m, with solutions $J_m(nr)$ and $Y_m(nr)$. J_m is finite and Y_m is infinite when $r = 0$, so that we shall usually require only the J_m solutions. The final form of ϕ is therefore

$$\phi = \frac{J_m}{Y_m}(nr)\frac{\cos}{\sin}m\theta\frac{\cos}{\sin}qz\frac{\cos}{\sin}cpt \quad . \quad . \quad (35)$$

If ϕ is to be single valued, m must be an integer; but n, q and p may be arbitrary provided that $n^2 = p^2 - q^2$. Hyperbolic modifications of (35) are possible, similar in all respects to (31) and (32).

Our final solution is one in spherical polar coordinates r, θ, ψ. The equation of wave motion (22) has a solution $R(r)\,\Theta(\theta)\,\Psi(\psi)\,T(t)$, where

$$\frac{d^2T}{dt^2} = -c^2p^2T , \frac{d^2\Psi}{d\psi^2} = -m^2\Psi,$$

$$\frac{1}{\sin\theta}\frac{d}{d\theta}\left(\sin\theta\frac{d\Theta}{d\theta}\right) + \left\{n(n+1) - \frac{m^2}{\sin^2\theta}\right\}\Theta = 0,$$

$$\frac{d^2R}{dr^2} + \frac{2}{r}\frac{dR}{dr} + \left\{p^2 - \frac{n(n+1)}{r^2}\right\}R = 0.$$

* See Ince, *Integration of Ordinary Differential Equations*, p. 127.

m, n and p are arbitrary constants, but if $\Psi(\psi)$ is to be single valued, m must be integral. The first two of these equations present no difficulties. The θ-equation is the generalised Legendre's Equation * with solution

$$\Theta(\theta) = P_n{}^m (\cos \theta),$$

and if Θ is to be finite everywhere, n must be a positive integer. When $m = 0$ and n is integral, $P_n{}^m (\cos \theta)$ reduces to a polynomial in $\cos \theta$ of degree n, known as the Legendre's polynomial $P_n (\cos \theta)$. For other integral values of m, $P_n{}^m (\cos \theta)$ is defined by the equation

$$P_n{}^m(\cos \theta) = \sin^m \theta \, \frac{d^m}{d(\cos \theta)^m} \{P_n(\cos \theta)\}.$$

A few values of $P_n (\cos \theta)$ and $P_n{}^m (\cos \theta)$ are given below, for small integral values of n and m. When $m > n$, $P_n{}^m (\cos \theta)$ vanishes identically.

$$P_0 (\cos \theta) = 1$$
$$P_1 (\cos \theta) = \cos \theta$$
$$P_2 (\cos \theta) = \tfrac{1}{2} (3 \cos^2 \theta - 1)$$
$$P_3 (\cos \theta) = \tfrac{1}{2} (5 \cos^3 \theta - 3 \cos \theta)$$
$$P_4 (\cos \theta) = \tfrac{1}{8} (35 \cos^4 \theta - 30 \cos^2 \theta + 3)$$
$$P_1{}^1 (\cos \theta) = \sin \theta$$
$$P_2{}^1 (\cos \theta) = 3 \sin \theta \cos \theta$$
$$P_3{}^1 (\cos \theta) = \tfrac{3}{2} \sin \theta (5 \cos^2 \theta - 1)$$
$$P_2{}^2 (\cos \theta) = 3 \sin^2 \theta.$$

To solve the R-equation put $R(r) = r^{-1/2}S(r)$, and we find that the equation for $S(r)$ is just Bessel's equation

$$\frac{d^2S}{dr^2} + \frac{1}{r}\frac{dS}{dr} + \left\{ p^2 - \frac{(n+\tfrac{1}{2})^2}{r^2} \right\} S = 0.$$

Therefore $S(r) = J_{n+1/2}(pr)$ or $Y_{n+1/2}(pr)$.

---

* See Ince, *Integration of Ordinary Differential Equations*, p. 119, for the case $m = 0$.

Collecting the various terms, the complete solution, apart from hyperbolic modifications, is seen to be

$$\phi = r^{-1/2} \frac{J_{n+1/2}}{Y_{n+1/2}} (pr) P_n{}^m (\cos\theta) \frac{\cos}{\sin} m\psi \frac{\cos}{\sin} cpt. \qquad (36)$$

If ϕ has axial symmetry, we must only take functions with $m = 0$, and if it has spherical symmetry, terms with $m = n = 0$. Now $J_{1/2}(z) = \sqrt{(2/\pi z)} \sin z$, and also $Y_{1/2}(z) = -\sqrt{(2/\pi z)} \cos z$, so that this becomes

$$\phi = r^{-1} \frac{\cos}{\sin} pr \frac{\cos}{\sin} cpt. \qquad . \qquad . \qquad (37)$$

A solution finite at the origin is obtained by omitting the $\cos pr$ term.

§ 8. We shall now gather together for future reference the solutions obtained in the preceding pages.

Progressive waves

1 dimension

$$\frac{\partial^2 \phi}{\partial x^2} = \frac{1}{c^2} \frac{\partial^2 \phi}{\partial t^2}$$

$$\phi = f(x - ct) + g(x + ct) \qquad . \qquad . \qquad (17)$$

2 dimensions

$$\frac{\partial^2 \phi}{\partial x^2} + \frac{\partial^2 \phi}{\partial y^2} = \frac{1}{c^2} \frac{\partial^2 \phi}{\partial t^2}$$

$$\phi = f(lx + my - ct) + g(lx + my + ct), \; l^2 + m^2 = 1 \; . \qquad (19)$$

3 dimensions

$$\frac{\partial^2 \phi}{\partial x^2} + \frac{\partial^2 \phi}{\partial y^2} + \frac{\partial^2 \phi}{\partial z^2} = \frac{1}{c^2} \frac{\partial^2 \phi}{\partial t^2}$$

$$\phi = f(lx + my + nz - ct) + g(lx + my + nz + ct), \; l^2 + m^2 + n^2 = 1 \qquad (21)$$

3 dimensions, spherical symmetry

$$\frac{\partial^2 \phi}{\partial r^2} + \frac{2}{r} \frac{\partial \phi}{\partial r} = \frac{1}{c^2} \frac{\partial^2 \phi}{\partial t^2}, \; \phi = \frac{1}{r} f(r - ct) + \frac{1}{r} g(r + ct) \qquad . \qquad (24)$$

Stationary waves

1 dimension

$$\frac{\partial^2 \phi}{\partial x^2} = \frac{1}{c^2}\frac{\partial^2 \phi}{\partial t^2} \ ,$$

$$\begin{cases} \phi = \frac{\cos}{\sin} px \frac{\cos}{\sin} cpt \quad . \quad (27) \\[2mm] \phi = e^{\pm px}\, e^{\pm cpt} \quad\quad . \quad (28) \end{cases}$$

2 dimensions

$$\frac{\partial^2 \phi}{\partial x^2} + \frac{\partial^2 \phi}{\partial y^2} = \frac{1}{c^2}\frac{\partial^2 \phi}{\partial t^2} \ ,$$

$$\begin{cases} \phi = \frac{\cos}{\sin} px \frac{\cos}{\sin} qy \frac{\cos}{\sin} rct,\ p^2+q^2=r^2 \\ \hspace{8cm} (29) \\[2mm] \phi = \frac{\cos}{\sin} px\, e^{\pm qy} \frac{\cos}{\sin} rct,\ p^2-q^2 = r^2 \\ \hspace{8cm} (30) \end{cases}$$

3 dimensions

$$\frac{\partial^2 \phi}{\partial x^2} + \frac{\partial^2 \phi}{\partial y^2} + \frac{\partial^2 \phi}{\partial z^2} = \frac{1}{c^2}\frac{\partial^2 \phi}{\partial t^2},$$

$$\begin{cases} \phi = \frac{\cos}{\sin} px \frac{\cos}{\sin} qy \frac{\cos}{\sin} rz \frac{\cos}{\sin} sct, \\ \hspace{2cm} p^2+q^2+r^2=s^2 \ . \quad (31) \\[2mm] \phi = \frac{\cosh}{\sinh} px\, e^{\pm qy} \frac{\cos}{\sin} rz \frac{\cos}{\sin} sct, \\ \hspace{2cm} -p^2-q^2+r^2=s^2 \ . \quad (32) \end{cases}$$

Plane Polar Coordinates (r, θ)

$$\frac{\partial^2 \phi}{\partial r^2} + \frac{1}{r}\frac{\partial \phi}{\partial r} + \frac{1}{r^2}\frac{\partial^2 \phi}{\partial \theta^2} = \frac{1}{c^2}\frac{\partial^2 \phi}{\partial t^2} \ , \quad \phi = \frac{J_m}{Y_m}(nr)\frac{\cos}{\sin} m\theta \frac{\cos}{\sin} cnt.$$

$$\hspace{12cm} (35a)$$

Cylindrical polar coordinates (r, θ, z)

$$\frac{\partial^2 \phi}{\partial r^2} + \frac{1}{r}\frac{\partial \phi}{\partial r} + \frac{1}{r^2}\frac{\partial^2 \phi}{\partial \theta^2} + \frac{\partial^2 \phi}{\partial z^2} = \frac{1}{c^2}\frac{\partial^2 \phi}{\partial t^2} \ ,$$

$$\phi = \frac{J_m}{Y_m}(nr)\frac{\cos}{\sin} m\theta \frac{\cos}{\sin} qz \frac{\cos}{\sin} cpt,\ n^2 = p^2-q^2 \ . \quad (35b)$$

Spherical Polar Coordinates (r, θ, ψ)

$$\frac{\partial^2 \phi}{\partial r^2} + \frac{2}{r}\frac{\partial \phi}{\partial r} + \frac{1}{r^2 \sin\theta}\frac{\partial}{\partial \theta}\left(\sin\theta \frac{\partial \phi}{\partial \theta}\right) + \frac{1}{r^2 \sin^2\theta}\frac{\partial^2 \phi}{\partial \psi^2} = \frac{1}{c^2}\frac{\partial^2 \phi}{\partial t^2} \ ,$$

$$\phi = r^{-1/2}\frac{J_{n+1/2}}{Y_{n+1/2}}(pr)P_n{}^m(\cos\theta)\frac{\cos}{\sin} m\psi \frac{\cos}{\sin} cpt \ . \quad (36)$$

Spherical symmetry

$$\frac{\partial^2 \phi}{\partial r^2} + \frac{2}{r}\frac{\partial \phi}{\partial r} = \frac{1}{c^2}\frac{\partial^2 \phi}{\partial t^2} , \qquad \phi = r^{-1} \frac{\cos}{\sin} pr \frac{\cos}{\sin} cpt . \quad (37)$$

It should be noted that there are exponential modifications of all the above equations.

In solving problems, we shall more often require progressive type solutions in cases where the variables x, y, z are allowed an infinite range of values, and stationary type solutions when their allowed range is finite.

§ 9. There is an important modification of the equation of wave motion which arises when friction, or some other dissipative force, produces a damping. The damping effect is usually allowed for (see e.g. Chapter II and elsewhere) by a term of the form $k\dfrac{\partial \phi}{\partial t}$, which will arise when the damping force is proportional to the velocity of the vibrations. The revised form of the fundamental equation, known as the **equation of telegraphy,** is

$$\nabla^2 \phi = \frac{1}{c^2}\left\{ \frac{\partial^2 \phi}{\partial t^2} + k\frac{\partial \phi}{\partial t} \right\}. \quad . \quad . \quad (38)$$

If we omit the term $\dfrac{\partial^2 \phi}{\partial t^2}$ this equation is the same as that occurring in the flow of heat. If we put $\phi = u\,e^{-kt/2}$, we obtain an equation for u of the form

$$\nabla^2 u = \frac{1}{c^2}\left\{ \frac{\partial^2 u}{\partial t^2} - \frac{1}{4}k^2 u \right\}. \quad . \quad . \quad (39)$$

Very often k is so small that we may neglect k^2, and then (39) is in the standard form which we have discussed in § **8,** and the solutions given there will apply. In such a case the presence of the dissipative term is shown by a decay factor $e^{-kt/2}$. If this is written in the form e^{-t/t_0}, then $t_0(= 2/k)$ is called the **modulus of decay.** When the term in k^2 may not be neglected, we have to solve (38) and the method of separation of variables usually enables a satisfactory solution to be obtained without much difficulty.

There is an alternative solution to the equation of telegraphy that is sometimes useful. Taking the case of one dimension, and supposing that k is so small that k^2 may be neglected, we have shown that the solution of (38) may be written in the form

$$\phi = e^{-kt/2} f(x-ct), \qquad . \qquad . \qquad . \qquad . \qquad (40)$$

where f is any function. Since f is arbitrary, we can put

$$f(x-ct) = e^{-\frac{k}{2c}(x-ct)} g(x-ct),$$

and g is now an arbitrary function. Substituting this in (40) we get

$$\phi = e^{-kx/2c} g(x-ct). \qquad . \qquad . \qquad . \qquad (41)$$

This expression resembles (40) except that the exponential factor varies with x instead of with t.

§ **10.** Most of the waves with which we shall be concerned in later chapters will be harmonic. This is partly because, as we have seen in § 8, harmonic functions arise very naturally when we try to solve the equation of wave motion ; it is also due to the fact that by means of a Fourier analysis, any function may be split into harmonic components, and hence by the principle of superposition, any wave may be regarded as the resultant of a set of harmonic waves.

When dealing with progressive waves of harmonic type there is one simplification that is often useful and which is especially important in the electromagnetic theory of light waves. We have seen in (11) that a progressive harmonic wave in one dimension can be represented by $\phi = a \cos 2\pi(kx-nt)$. If we allow for a phase ϵ, it will be written $\phi = a \cos \{2\pi(kx-nt)+\epsilon\}$. Now this latter function may be regarded as the real part of the complex quantity $a\, e^{\pm i\{2\pi(kx-nt)+\epsilon\}}$. It is most convenient for our subsequent work if we choose the minus sign and also absorb the phase ϵ and the amplitude a into one complex number A. We shall then write

$$\phi = A \, e^{2\pi i(nt - kx)} \, , \, A = a \, e^{-i\epsilon} \, . \quad . \quad . \quad (42)$$

This complex quantity is itself a solution of the equation of wave motion, as can easily be seen by substitution, and consequently both its real and imaginary parts are also solutions. Since all our equations in ϕ are linear, <u>it is possible to use (42) itself as a solution of the equation of wave motion, instead of its real part.</u> In any equation in which ϕ appears to the first degree, we can, if we wish, use the function (42) and assume that we always refer to the real part, or we can just use (42) as it stands, without reference to its real or imaginary parts. In such a case the apparent amplitude A is usually complex, and since $A = a \, e^{-i\epsilon}$, we can say that $|A|$ is the true amplitude, and $-arg \, A$ is the true phase. The velocity, of course, as given by (7) and (10), is n/k.

We can extend this representation of ϕ to cover waves travelling in the opposite direction by using in such a case

$$\phi = A \, e^{2\pi i(nt + kx)} \, . \quad . \quad . \quad . \quad (43)$$

There is obviously no reason why we should not extend this to two or three dimensions. For instance, in three dimensions

$$\phi = A \, e^{2\pi i\{nt - (px + qy + rz)\}} \quad . \quad . \quad (44)$$

would represent a harmonic wave with amplitude A moving with velocity $n/\sqrt{(p^2 + q^2 + r^2)}$ in the direction $x : y : z = p : q : r$.

§ 11. We shall conclude this chapter with an example. Let us find a solution of $\dfrac{\partial^2 \phi}{\partial x^2} + \dfrac{\partial^2 \phi}{\partial y^2} = \dfrac{1}{c^2} \dfrac{\partial^2 \phi}{\partial t^2}$ such that ϕ vanishes on the lines $x = 0$, $x = a$, $y = 0$, $y = b$. Since

B

the lines $x = 0$, a, and $y = 0$, b are nodal lines, our solution must be of the stationary type. Referring to § **8**, equation (29), we see that possible solutions are

$$\phi = \frac{\cos}{\sin} px \frac{\cos}{\sin} qy \frac{\cos}{\sin} rct \text{ , where } p^2 + q^2 = r^2.$$

Since ϕ is identically zero at $x = 0$, and $y = 0$, we shall have to take the sine rather than the cosine in the first two factors. Further, since at $x = a$, $\phi = 0$ for all values of y, therefore

$$\sin pa = 0.$$

Similarly, $\qquad \sin qb = 0.$

Hence $p = m\pi/a$, and $q = n\pi/b$, m and n being integers. A solution satisfying all the conditions is therefore

$$\phi = \sin \frac{m\pi x}{a} \sin \frac{n\pi y}{b} \frac{\cos}{\sin} rct \text{ ,}$$

where $\qquad r^2 = \pi^2(m^2/a^2 + n^2/b^2).$

The most general solution is the sum of an arbitrary number of such terms, e.g.

$$\phi = \underset{m,\, n}{\Sigma} \sin \frac{m\pi x}{a} \sin \frac{n\pi y}{b} \{C_{mn} \cos rct + D_{mn} \sin rct\}. \qquad (45)$$

At $t = 0$, this gives

$$[\phi]_{t=0} = \Sigma C_{mn} \sin \frac{m\pi x}{a} \sin \frac{n\pi y}{b},$$

$$[\dot{\phi}]_{t=0} = \Sigma rc D_{mn} \sin \frac{m\pi x}{a} \sin \frac{n\pi y}{b}.$$

By suitable choice of the constants C_{mn} and D_{mn} we can make ϕ and $\dot{\phi}$ have any chosen form at $t = 0$. The value at any subsequent time is then given by (45).

§ 12.   Examples

(1) Show that $\phi = f(x \cos \theta + y \sin \theta - ct)$ represents a wave in two dimensions, the direction of propagation making an angle θ with the axis of x.

(2) Show that $\phi = a \cos (lx + my - ct)$ is a wave in two dimensions and find its wavelength.

(3) What is the wavelength and velocity of the system of plane waves $\phi = a \sin (Ax + By + Cz - Dt)$?

(4) Show that three equivalent harmonic waves with 120° phase between each pair have zero sum.

(5) Show that $\phi = r^{-1/2} \cos \frac{1}{2}\theta f(r \pm ct)$ is a progressive type wave in two dimensions, r and θ being plane polar coordinates, and f being an arbitrary function. By superposing two of these waves in which f is a harmonic function, obtain a stationary wave, and draw its nodal lines. *Note that this is not a single-valued function unless we put restrictions upon the allowed range of θ.*

(6) By taking the special case of $f(x) = g(x) = \sin px$ in equation (24), show that it reduces to the result of equation (36) in which $m = n = 0$. Use the relation

$$J_{1/2}(x) = \sqrt{\left(\frac{2}{\pi x}\right)} \sin x.$$

(7) Find a solution of $\dfrac{\partial^2 \phi}{\partial x^2} + \dfrac{1}{c^2} \dfrac{\partial^2 \phi}{\partial t^2} = 0$, such that $\phi = 0$ when $t = \infty$, and $\phi = 0$ when $x = 0$.

(8) Find a solution of $\dfrac{\partial^2 \phi}{\partial x^2} = \dfrac{1}{c^2} \dfrac{\partial^2 \phi}{\partial t^2}$ such that $\phi = 0$ when $x = +\infty$ or $t = +\infty$.

(9) Solve the equation $\dfrac{\partial^2 z}{\partial t^2} = c^2 \dfrac{\partial^2 z}{\partial x^2}$ given that z is never infinite for real values of x and t, and $z = 0$ when $x = 0$, or when $t = 0$.

(10) Solve $\dfrac{\partial^2 V}{\partial x^2} = \dfrac{\partial V}{\partial t}$ given that $V = 0$ when $t = \infty$ and when $x = 0$, and when $x = l$.

(11) x, y, z are given in terms of the three quantities ξ, η, ζ by the equations

$$x = a \sinh \xi \sin \eta \cos \zeta$$
$$y = a \sinh \xi \sin \eta \sin \zeta$$
$$z = a \cosh \xi \cos \eta$$

Show that the equation $\dfrac{\partial^2 \phi}{\partial x^2} + \dfrac{\partial^2 \phi}{\partial y^2} + \dfrac{\partial^2 \phi}{\partial z^2} = \dfrac{1}{c^2} \dfrac{\partial^2 \phi}{\partial t^2}$ is of the correct form for solution by the method of separation of variables, when ξ, η, ζ are used as the independent variables. Write down the subsidiary equations into which the whole equation breaks down.

12. Show that the equation of telegraphy (38) in one dimension has solutions of the form

$$\phi = \genfrac{}{}{0pt}{}{\cos}{\sin} mx \genfrac{}{}{0pt}{}{\cos}{\sin} pt \, e^{-kt/2},$$

where m and p are constants satisfying the equation $p^2 = m^2 c^2 - \frac{1}{4}k^2$.

[ANSWERS: 2. $2\pi/(l^2 + m^2)^{\frac{1}{2}}$; 3. $\lambda = 2\pi/(A^2 + B^2 + C^2)^{\frac{1}{2}}$, vel. $= \lambda D/2\pi$; 7. $A \sin nx \, e^{-cnt}$; 8. $Ae^{-n(x+ct)}$; 9. $A \sin px \sin cpt$; 10. $Ae^{-p^2 t} \sin px$, $p = \pi/l$, $2\pi/l$, ..; 11. Show that $\xi = $ const., $\eta = $ const., $\zeta = $ const. form an orthogonal system of coordinates, and transform $\nabla^2 \phi$ in terms of ξ, η, ζ as in Rutherford, Vector Methods, § 47. The result is $\phi = X(\xi)Y(\eta)Z(\zeta)T(t)$, where m, p and q are arbitrary constants, and

$$\frac{1}{\sinh \xi} \frac{d}{d\xi} \sinh \xi \frac{dX}{d\xi} - \frac{m^2}{\sinh^2 \xi} X + p^2 \sinh^2 \xi \, X = q^2 X,$$

$$\frac{1}{\sin \eta} \frac{d}{d\eta} \sin \eta \frac{dY}{d\eta} - \frac{m^2}{\sin^2 \eta} Y + p^2 \sin^2 \eta \, Y = -q^2 Y,$$

$$\frac{d^2 Z}{dz^2} = -m^2 Z, \qquad \frac{d^2 T}{dt^2} = -\frac{c^2 p^2}{a^2} T.]$$

CHAPTER II

WAVES ON STRINGS

§ 13. In this chapter we shall discuss the transverse vibrations of a heavy string of mass ρ per unit length. By **transverse** vibrations we mean vibrations in which the displacement of each particle of the string is in a direction perpendicular to the length. When the displacement is in the same direction as the string, we call the waves **longitudinal** ; these waves will be discussed in Chapter IV. We shall neglect the effect of gravity ; in practice this may be approximately achieved by supposing that the whole motion takes place on a smooth horizontal plane.

In order that a wave may travel along the string, it is necessary that the string should be at least slightly extensible ; in our calculations, however, we shall assume that the tension does not change appreciably from its normal value F. The condition for this (see § 14) is that the wave disturbance is not too large.

Let us consider the motion of a small element of the string PQ (fig. 1) of length ds. Suppose that in the equilibrium state the string lies along the axis of x, and that PQ is originally at P_0Q_0. Let the displacement of PQ from the x axis be denoted by y. Then we shall obtain an equation for the motion of PQ in terms of the tension and density of the string. The forces acting on this element, when the string is vibrating, are merely the two tensions F acting along the tangents at P and Q as shown in the figure ; let ψ and $\psi+d\psi$ be the angles made by these two tangents with the x axis. We can easily write down the equation of motion of the element PQ in the y direction; for the resultant force acting parallel to the y axis is $F \sin (\psi + d\psi) - F \sin \psi$. Neglecting squares of small quantities, this is $F \cos \psi\, d\psi$. The equation of motion is therefore

$$F \cos \psi\, d\psi = \rho ds \frac{\partial^2 y}{\partial t^2} \quad \cdot \quad \cdot \quad \cdot \quad (1)$$

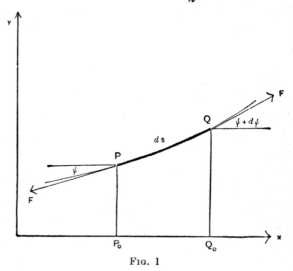

Fig. 1

Now $\tan \psi = \dfrac{\partial y}{\partial x}$, so that $sec^2\psi d\psi = \dfrac{\partial^2 y}{\partial x^2}dx$, and so, from (1)

$$\rho \frac{\partial^2 y}{\partial t^2} = F \cos^3\psi \frac{\partial^2 y}{\partial x^2} \cdot \frac{\partial x}{\partial s}$$

$$= F \cos^4\psi \frac{\partial^2 y}{\partial x^2} \quad \cdot \quad \cdot \quad \cdot \quad (2)$$

But $\cos^2\psi = \left\{ 1 + \left(\dfrac{\partial y}{\partial x} \right)^2 \right\}^{-1}$, so that if the displacements are small enough for us to neglect $\left(\dfrac{\partial y}{\partial x}\right)^2$ compared with unity, we may write (2) in the standard form for wave motion * (Chapter I, § **5**), viz.,

$$\frac{\partial^2 y}{\partial x^2} = \frac{1}{c^2} \frac{\partial^2 y}{\partial t^2} \text{ , where } c^2 = F/\rho \text{ . . (3)}$$

It follows from Chapter I, equation (17) that the general solution of this equation may be put in the form

$$y = f(x-ct) + g(x+ct), \text{ . . . (4)}$$

f and g being arbitrary functions. $f(x-ct)$ represents a progressive wave travelling in the positive direction of the x axis with velocity c, and $g(x+ct)$ represents a progressive wave with the same velocity in the negative direction of x. Thus waves of any shape can travel in either direction with velocity $c = \sqrt{(F/\rho)}$, and without change of form. A more complete discussion, in which we did not neglect terms of the second order, would show us that the velocity was not quite independent of the shape, and indeed, that the wave profile would change slowly with the time. These corrections are difficult to apply, and we shall be content with (4), which is, indeed, an excellent approximation except where there is a sudden " kink " in y, in which case we cannot neglect $\left(\dfrac{\partial y}{\partial x}\right)^2$.

§ **14.** Since the velocity of any point of the string is $\dot{y}$, we can soon determine the kinetic energy of vibration. It is

$$T = \int \tfrac{1}{2} \rho \dot{y}^2 dx \text{ . . . . (5)}$$

* The student who is interested in geometry will be able to prove that the two tensions at P and Q are together equivalent to a single force of magnitude Fds/R, where R is the radius of curvature of the string. This force acts perpendicularly to PQ. Putting

$R = \left\{ 1 + \left(\dfrac{\partial y}{\partial x}\right)^2 \right\}^{3/2} \Big/ \dfrac{\partial^2 y}{\partial x^2}$, and neglecting $\left(\dfrac{\partial y}{\partial x}\right)^2$, we obtain (3).

The potential energy V is found by considering the increase of length of the element PQ. This element has increased its length from dx to ds. We have therefore done an amount of work $F(ds-dx)$. Summing for all the elements of the string, we obtain the formula

$$V = \int F(ds - dx) = \int F \left\{ \sqrt{\left(1 + \left(\frac{\partial y}{\partial x}\right)^2\right)} - 1 \right\} dx$$

$$= \tfrac{1}{2}F \int \left(\frac{\partial y}{\partial x}\right)^2 dx, \text{ approximately.} \qquad . \qquad (6)$$

The integrations in (5) and (6) are both taken over the length of the string.

With a progressive wave $y = f(x-ct)$, these equations give

$$T = \int \tfrac{1}{2}\rho c^2 (f')^2 dx = \tfrac{1}{2}F \int (f')^2 dx \qquad . \qquad . \qquad (7)$$

$$V = \tfrac{1}{2}F \int (f')^2 dx \qquad . \qquad . \qquad . \qquad . \qquad (8)$$

Thus the kinetic and potential energies are equal. The same result applies to the progressive wave $y = g(x+ct)$, but it does not, in general, apply to the stationary type waves $y = f(x-ct) + g(x+ct)$.

We can now decide whether our initial assumption is correct, that the tension remains effectively constant. If the string is elastic, the change in tension will be proportional to the change in length. We have seen in (6) that the change in length of an element dx is $\dfrac{1}{2} \left(\dfrac{\partial y}{\partial x}\right)^2 dx$.

Thus, provided that $\dfrac{\partial y}{\partial x}$ is of the first order of small quantities, the change of tension is of the second order, and may safely be neglected. This assumption is equivalent to asserting that the wave profile does not have any large " kinks," but has a relatively gradual variation with x.

§ 15. The functions f and g of (4) are arbitrary. But they may be fixed by a knowledge of the initial conditions. Thus, with a string of unlimited length, such that $y_{t=0} = \phi(x)$, $\dot{y}_{t=0} = \psi(x)$,* we must have, from (4),

$$f(x) + g(x) = \phi(x),$$
$$-c f'(x) + c g'(x) = \psi(x).$$

Integrating this last equation we have

$$-f(x) + g(x) = (1/c) \int^x \psi(x)dx,$$

and so

$$f(x) = \frac{1}{2} \left\{ \phi(x) - \frac{1}{c} \int^x \psi(x)dx \right\},$$

$$g(x) = \frac{1}{2} \left\{ \phi(x) + \frac{1}{c} \int^x \psi(x)dx \right\}.$$

The displacement at any subsequent time t is therefore

$$y = \frac{1}{2} \left\{ \phi(x-ct) + \phi(x+ct) - \frac{1}{c} \int^{x-ct} \psi(x)dx + \frac{1}{c} \int^{x+ct} \psi(x)dx \right\}$$

$$= \frac{1}{2} \left\{ \phi(x-ct) + \phi(x+ct) + \frac{1}{c} \int_{x-ct}^{x+ct} \psi(x)dx \right\}. \qquad . \qquad . \qquad (9)$$

§ 16. The discussion above applies specifically to strings of infinite length. Before we discuss strings of finite length, we shall solve two problems of reflection of waves from a discontinuity in the string. The first is when two strings of different densities are joined together, and the second is when a mass is concentrated at a point of the string. In each case we shall find that an incident wave gives rise to a reflected and a transmitted wave.

Consider first, then, the case of two semi-infinite strings 1 and 2 joined at the origin (fig. 2). Let the

* This function $\psi(x)$ must be distinguished from the angle ψ in § 13.

densities of the two strings be ρ_1 and ρ_2. Denote the displacements in the two strings by y_1 and y_2. Let us suppose that a train of harmonic waves is incident from the negative direction of x. When these waves meet the change of wire, they will suffer partial reflection and partial transmission. If we choose the exponential functions of § **10** to represent each of these waves, we may write

$$y_1 = y_{\text{incident}} + y_{\text{reflected}}$$
$$y_2 = y_{\text{transmitted}} \qquad . \qquad . \qquad (10)$$

where

$$y_{\text{incident}} = A_1 e^{2\pi i(nt - k_1 x)}$$
$$y_{\text{reflected}} = B_1 e^{2\pi i(nt + k_1 x)}$$
$$y_{\text{transmitted}} = A_2 e^{2\pi i(nt - k_2 x)} \qquad . \qquad . \qquad (11)$$

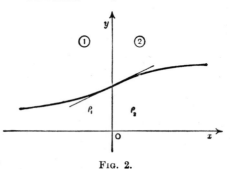

Fig. 2.

A_1 is real, but A_2 and B_1 may be complex. According to § **10** equation (42), the arguments of A_2 and B_1 will give their phases relative to the incident wave. All three waves in (11) must have the same frequency n, but since the velocities in the two wires are different, they will have different wavelengths $1/k_1$ and $1/k_2$. The reflected wave must, of course, have the same wavelength as the incident wave. Since the velocities of the two types of waves are n/k_1 and n/k_2 (Chapter I, equations (7) and (10)), and we have shown in (3) that $c^2 = F/\rho$, therefore

$$k_1{}^2/k_2{}^2 = \rho_1/\rho_2 . \qquad . \qquad . \qquad (12)$$

In order to determine A_2 and B_1 we use what are known as the **boundary conditions**. These are the conditions which must hold at the boundary point $x=0$. Since the two strings are continuous, we must have $y_1 = y_2$ identically for all values of t, and also the two slopes must be the same, so that $\dfrac{\partial y_1}{\partial x} = \dfrac{\partial y_2}{\partial x}$ for all t. If this latter condition were not satisfied, we should have a finite force acting on an infinitesimal piece of wire at the common point, thus giving it infinite acceleration. We shall often meet boundary conditions in other parts of this book ; their precise form will depend of course upon the particular problem under discussion. In the present case, the two boundary conditions give

$$A_1 + B_1 = A_2,$$
$$2\pi i(-k_1 A_1 + k_1 B_1) = 2\pi i(-k_2 A_2).$$

These equations have a solution

$$\frac{B_1}{A_1} = \frac{k_1 - k_2}{k_1 + k_2} , \quad \frac{A_2}{A_1} = \frac{2k_1}{k_1 + k_2} \quad . \quad . \quad (13)$$

Since k_1, k_2 and A_1 are real, this shows that B_1 and A_2 are both real. A_2 is positive for all k_1 and k_2, but B_1 is positive if $k_1 > k_2$, and negative if $k_1 < k_2$. Thus the transmitted wave is always in phase with the incident wave, but the reflected wave is in phase only when the incident wave is in the denser medium ; otherwise it is exactly out of phase.

The **coefficient of reflection** R is defined to be the ratio, $|B_1/A_1|^2$, i.e. $\left(\dfrac{k_1 - k_2}{k_1 + k_2}\right)^2$ which, by (12), we may write

$$\left(\frac{\sqrt{\rho_1} - \sqrt{\rho_2}}{\sqrt{\rho_1} + \sqrt{\rho_2}}\right)^2 . \quad . \quad . \quad (14)$$

Since, from (7) and (8), the energy of a progressive wave is proportional to the square of its amplitude, it follows that R represents the ratio of reflected energy to incident ene·gy. Similarly, since no energy is wasted, the **coefficient of transmission** T, which gives the ratio of transmitted energy to incident energy, is equal to $1-R$,

i.e. $$\frac{4\sqrt{\rho_1}\sqrt{\rho_2}}{(\sqrt{\rho_1}+\sqrt{\rho_2})^2} \qquad . \qquad . \qquad . \qquad (15)$$

§ **17.** A similar discussion can be given for the case of a mass M concentrated at a point of the string. Let us take the equilibrium position of the mass to be the origin (fig. 3) and suppose that the string is identical on the two

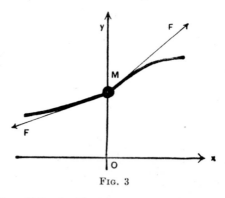

Fig. 3

sides. Then if the incident wave comes from the negative side of the origin, we may write, just as in (10) and (11):

$$y_1 = y_{\text{incident}} + y_{\text{reflected}}$$
$$y_2 = y_{\text{transmitted}}$$

where

$$y_{\text{incident}} = A_1 e^{2\pi i(nt - kx)}$$
$$y_{\text{reflected}} = B_1 e^{2\pi i(nt + kx)}$$
$$y_{\text{transmitted}} = A_2 e^{2\pi i(nt - kx)} \qquad . \qquad . \qquad . \qquad (16)$$

The boundary conditions are that for all values of t

(i) $$[y_1]_{x=0} = [y_2]_{x=0} \qquad . \qquad . \qquad . \qquad . \qquad (17)$$

(ii) $$F\left[\frac{\partial y_2}{\partial x} - \frac{\partial y_1}{\partial x}\right]_{x=0} = M\left[\frac{\partial^2 y_2}{\partial t^2}\right]_{x=0} . \qquad . \qquad (18)$$

The first equation expresses the continuity of the string and the second is the equation of motion of the mass M. We can see this as follows: the net force on M is the difference of the components of F on either side, so that if ψ_1 and ψ_2 are the angles made with the x axis, we have

$$M \left[\frac{\partial^2 y_2}{\partial t^2} \right]_{x=0} = F (\sin \psi_2 - \sin \psi_1).$$

Since ψ_1 and ψ_2 are small, we may put $\sin \psi_2 = \tan \psi_2 = \dfrac{\partial y_2}{\partial x}$, $\sin \psi_1 = \dfrac{\partial y_1}{\partial x}$, and (18) is then obtained.

Substituting from (16) into (17) and (18), and cancelling the term $e^{2\pi i n t}$, which is common to both sides, we find

$$A_1 + B_1 = A_2,$$
$$2\pi i k F (A_2 - A_1 + B_1) = 4\pi^2 n^2 M A_2.$$

Let us write $\qquad \pi n^2 M / k F = p$ . . . . (19)

A solution of the equations then gives

$$\frac{B_1}{A_1} = \frac{-ip}{1+ip} = \frac{-p^2-ip}{1+p^2} \qquad . \quad . \quad (20)$$

$$\frac{A_2}{A_1} = \frac{1}{1+ip} = \frac{1-ip}{1+p^2} \qquad . \quad . \quad (21)$$

In this problem, unlike the last, B_1 and A_2 are complex, so that there are phase changes. These phases (according to § 10) are given by the arguments of (20) and (21). They are therefore $\tan^{-1}(p)$ and $\tan^{-1}(-1/p)$ respectively. The coefficient of reflection R is $|B_1/A_1|^2$, which equals $p^2/(1+p^2)$, and the coefficient of transmission T is $1-R$, i.e. $1/(1+p^2)$. If we write $p = \tan \theta$, where $0 \leqslant \theta \leqslant \pi/2$, then we find that the phase changes are θ and $\pi/2 + \theta$, and also $R = \sin^2 \theta$, $T = \cos^2 \theta$.

§ 18. The two problems in §§ 16, 17 could be solved quite easily by taking a real form for each of the waves instead of the complex forms (11) and (16). The student is advised to solve these problems in this way, taking, for example, in § **17**, the forms

$$y_{\text{incident}} = a_1 \cos 2\pi(nt - kx)$$
$$y_{\text{reflected}} = b_1 \cos \{2\pi(nt + kx) + \epsilon\}$$
$$y_{\text{transmitted}} = a_2 \cos \{2\pi(nt - kx) + \eta\} \qquad . \qquad (22)$$

In most cases of progressive waves, however, the complex form is the easier to handle ; the reason for this is that exponentials are simpler than harmonic functions, and also the amplitude and phase are represented by one complex quantity rather than by two separate terms.

§ **19.** So far we have been dealing with strings of infinite length. When we deal with strings of finite length it is easier to use stationary type waves instead of progressive type. Let us now consider waves on a string of length l, fastened at the ends where $x = 0, l$. We have to find a solution of the equation (3), viz. $\dfrac{\partial^2 y}{\partial x^2} = \dfrac{1}{c^2} \dfrac{\partial^2 y}{\partial t^2}$, subject to the boundary conditions $y = 0$, at $x = 0, l$, for all t. Now by Chapter **I**, § **8**, we see that suitable solutions are of the type

$$\frac{\cos}{\sin} px \frac{\cos}{\sin} cpt.$$

It is clear that the cosine term in x will not satisfy the boundary condition at $x = 0$, and we may therefore write the solution

$$y = \sin px \, (a \cos cpt + b \sin cpt).$$

The constants a, b and p are arbitrary, but we have still to make $y = 0$ at $x = l$. This implies that $\sin pl = 0$, i.e. $pl = \pi, 2\pi, 3\pi. \ . \ . \ .$ It follows that the solution is

$$y = \sin \frac{r\pi x}{l} \left(a \cos \frac{r\pi ct}{l} + b \sin \frac{r\pi ct}{l} \right), \ r = 1,2,3, \ . \ . \ . \quad (23)$$

Each of the solutions (23) in which r may have any positive integral value, is known as a **normal mode** of vibration. The most general solution is the sum of any number of terms similar to (23) and may therefore be written

$$y = \sum_r \sin \frac{r\pi x}{l} \left\{ a_r \cos \frac{r\pi ct}{l} + b_r \sin \frac{r\pi ct}{l} \right\} \quad . \quad (24)$$

The values of a_r and b_r are determined from the initial conditions ; thus, when $t = 0$,

$$y_{t=0} = \sum_r a_r \sin \frac{r\pi x}{l} \quad . \qquad . \qquad . \qquad (25)$$

$$\dot{y}_{t=0} = \sum_r b_r \frac{r\pi c}{l} \sin \frac{r\pi x}{l} \quad . \qquad . \qquad . \qquad (26)$$

If we are told the initial velocity and shape of the string, then each a_r and b_r is found from (25) and (26), and hence the full solution is obtained. We shall write down the results for reference. If we suppose that when $t = 0$, $y = \phi(x)$, $\dot{y} = \psi(x)$, then the Fourier analysis represented by (25) and (26) gives

$$a_r = \frac{2}{l} \int_0^l \phi(x) \sin \frac{r\pi x}{l} \, dx$$

$$b_r = \frac{2}{r\pi c} \int_0^l \psi(x) \sin \frac{r\pi x}{l} \, dx \qquad . \qquad . \qquad (27)$$

In particular, if the string is released from rest when $t = 0$, every $b_r = 0$.

§ **20**. As an illustration of the theory of the last section, let us consider the case of a plucked string of length l released from rest when the midpoint is drawn aside through a distance h (fig. 4). In accordance with (25) and (26) we can assume that

$$y = \sum_{r=1}^{\infty} a_r \sin \frac{r\pi x}{l} \cos \frac{r\pi ct}{l} .$$

When $t = 0$, this reduces to $\Sigma_r a_r \sin \dfrac{r\pi x}{l}$, and the coefficients a_r have to be chosen so that this is identical with

$$y = \frac{2h}{l} x , \quad 0 \leqslant x \leqslant \tfrac{1}{2}l$$

$$y = \frac{2h}{l} (l-x) , \quad \tfrac{1}{2}l \leqslant x \leqslant l.$$

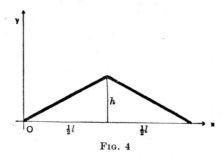

Fig. 4

If we multiply both sides of the equation $y = \Sigma_r a_r \sin \dfrac{r\pi x}{l}$ by $\sin \dfrac{r\pi x}{l}$, and integrate from $x = 0$ to $x = l$, as in the method of Fourier analysis, all the terms except one will disappear on the right-hand side, and we shall obtain

$$\frac{l}{2} a_r = \int_0^{l/2} \frac{2h}{l} x \sin \frac{r\pi x}{l} dx + \int_{l/2}^l \frac{2h}{l} (l-x) \sin \frac{r\pi x}{l} dx.$$

Whence

$$a_r = \frac{8h}{\pi^2 r^2} \sin \frac{r\pi}{2} \quad \text{when } r \text{ is odd,}$$

$$= 0 \quad \text{when } r \text{ is even.}$$

So the full solution, giving the value of y at all subsequent times, is

$$y = \frac{8h}{\pi^2} \sum_{n=0}^{\infty} \frac{1}{(2n+1)^2} \sin \frac{(2n+1)\pi}{2} \sin \frac{(2n+1)\pi x}{l} \cos \frac{(2n+1)\pi c t}{l}$$

$$(28)$$

Thus the value of y is the result of superposing certain normal modes with their appropriate amplitudes. These are known as the **partial amplitudes**. The partial amplitude of any selected normal mode (the rth for example), is just the coefficient a_r. In this example, a_r vanishes except when r is odd, and then a_r is proportional to $1/r^2$, so that the amplitude of the higher modes is relatively small.

§ 21. The rth normal mode (23) has a frequency $rc/2l$. Also, there are zero values of y (i.e. nodes) at the points $x = 0$, l/r, $2l/r$ .... $(r-1)l/r$, l. If the string is plucked with the finger lightly resting on the point l/r it will be found that this mode of vibration is excited. With even order vibrations (r even) the mid-point is a node, and with odd order vibrations it is an antinode.

We can find the energy associated with this mode of vibration most conveniently by rewriting (23) in the form

$$y = A \sin \frac{r\pi x}{l} \cos \left\{ \frac{r\pi ct}{l} + \epsilon \right\} \qquad . \qquad . \qquad (29)$$

Here A is the amplitude and ϵ is the phase. According to (5) the kinetic energy is

$$T = \frac{1}{2} \rho \int_0^l \dot{y}^2 \, dx = \frac{\pi^2 c^2 r^2 \rho}{4l} A^2 \sin^2 \left\{ \frac{r\pi ct}{l} + \epsilon \right\}. \quad (30)$$

Similarly, by (6) the potential energy is

$$V = \frac{1}{2} F \int_0^l \left(\frac{\partial y}{\partial x} \right)^2 dx = \frac{\pi^2 r^2 F}{4l} A^2 \cos^2 \left\{ \frac{r\pi ct}{l} + \epsilon \right\}. \quad (31)$$

Now by (3) $F/\rho = c^2$, and so the two coefficients in (30) and (31) are equal. The total energy of this vibration is therefore

$$\frac{\pi^2 c^2 r^2 \rho}{4l} A^2 \qquad . \qquad . \qquad . \qquad (32)$$

c

The total energy is thus proportional to the square of the amplitude and also to the square of the frequency. This is a result that we shall often find as we investigate various types of wave motion.

As a rule, however, there are several normal modes present at the same time, and we can then write the displacement (24) in the more convenient form

$$y = \sum_{r=1}^{\infty} A_r \sin \frac{r\pi x}{l} \cos \left\{ \frac{r\pi ct}{l} + \epsilon_r \right\}. \qquad (33)$$

A_r is the amplitude, and ϵ_r is the phase, of the rth normal mode. When we evaluate the kinetic energy as in (30) we find that the "cross-terms" vanish, since $\int_0^l \sin \frac{r\pi x}{l} \sin \frac{s\pi x}{l} \, dx = 0$, if $r \neq s$. Consequently the total kinetic energy is just

$$\frac{\pi^2 c^2 \rho}{4l} \sum r^2 A_r^2 \sin^2 \left\{ \frac{r\pi ct}{l} + \epsilon_r \right\},$$

and in a precisely similar way the total potential energy is

$$\frac{\pi^2 F}{4l} \sum r^2 A_r^2 \cos^2 \left\{ \frac{r\pi ct}{l} + \epsilon_r \right\}.$$

By addition we find that the total energy of vibration is

$$\frac{\pi^2 c^2 \rho}{4l} \sum r^2 A_r^2. \qquad (34)$$

This formula is important. It shows that the total energy is merely the sum of the energies obtained separately for each normal mode. It is due to this simple fact, which arises because there are no cross-terms involving $A_r A_s$, that the separate modes of vibration are called normal modes. It should be observed that this result holds for both the kinetic and potential energies separately as well as for their sum.

We have already seen that when a string vibrates more than one mode is usually excited. The lowest frequency, viz. $c/2l$, is called the **ground note**, or **fundamental**, and the others, with frequencies $rc/2l$, are **harmonics** or **overtones**. The frequency of the fundamental varies directly as the square root of the tension and inversely as the length and square root of the density. This is known as **Mersenne's law**. The **tone**, or quality, of a vibration is governed by the proportion of energy in each of the harmonics, and it is this that is characteristic of each musical instrument. The tone must be carefully distinguished from the **pitch**, which is merely the frequency of the fundamental.

We can use the results of (34) to determine the total energy in each normal mode of the vibrating string which we discussed in § **20**. According to (28) and (33) $A_{2n} = 0$, and $A_{2n+1} = \dfrac{8h}{\pi^2} \dfrac{1}{(2n+1)^2} \sin \dfrac{(2n+1)\pi}{2}$. Consequently, the total energy of the even modes is zero, and the energy of the $(2n+1)$th mode is $16c^2h^2\rho/(2n+1)^2\pi^2l$. This shows us that the main part of the energy is associated with the normal modes of low order. We can check these formulæ for the energies in this example quite easily. For the total energy of the whole vibration is the sum of the energies of each normal mode separately : i.e.

$$\text{total energy} = \frac{16c^\circ h^2 \rho}{\pi^2 l} \sum_{n=0}^{\infty} \frac{1}{(2n+1)^2}.$$

It is shown in books on algebra that the sum of the series $1/1^2+1/3^2+1/5^2+ \ldots$ is $\pi^2/8$. Hence the total energy is $2c^2h^2\rho/l$, i.e. $2Fh^2/l$. But the string was drawn aside and released from rest in the position of fig. 4, and at that moment the whole energy was in the form of potential energy. This potential energy is just F times the increase in length, i.e. $2F\{(l^2/4+h^2)^{1/2}-l/2\}$. A simple calculation shows that if we neglect powers of h above the second, as we have already done in our formulation of the equation of wave motion, this becomes $2Fh^2/l$, thus verifying our earlier result.

This particular example corresponds quite closely to the case of a violin string bowed at its mid-point. A listener would thus hear not only the fundamental, but also a variety of other frequencies, simply related to the fundamental numerically. This would not therefore be a pure note, though the small amount of the higher harmonics makes it much purer than that of many musical instruments, particularly a piano.

If the string had been bowed at some other point than its centre, the partial amplitudes would have been different, and thus the tone would be changed. By choosing the point properly any desired harmonic may be emphasised or diminished, a fact well known to musicians.

§ 22. We have seen in § 21 that it is most convenient to analyse the motion of a string of finite length in terms of its normal modes. According to (33) the rth mode is

$$y_r = A_r \sin \frac{r\pi x}{l} \cos \left\{ \frac{r\pi ct}{l} + \epsilon_r \right\}.$$

We often write this

$$y_r = \phi_r \sin \frac{r\pi x}{l} \qquad . \qquad . \qquad (35)$$

The expressions ϕ_r are known as the **normal coordinates** for the string. There are an infinite number of these coordinates, since there are an infinite number of degrees of freedom in a vibrating string. The advantage of using these coordinates can be seen from (30) and (31); if the displacement of the string is

$$y = \sum_{r=1}^{\infty} \phi_r \sin \frac{r\pi x}{l} \qquad . \qquad . \qquad (36)$$

then

$$T = \frac{1}{4} \rho l \underset{r}{\Sigma} \dot{\phi}_r{}^2$$

$$V = \frac{\pi^2 c^2 \rho}{4l} \underset{r}{\Sigma} r^2 \phi_r{}^2 \quad \cdot \quad \cdot \quad \cdot \quad (37)$$

The reason why we call ϕ_r a normal coordinate is now clear; for in mechanics the normal coordinates $q_1, q_2 \ldots q_n$ are suitable combinations of the original variables so that the kinetic and potential energies can be written in the form

$$T = a_1 \dot{q}_1{}^2 + a_2 \dot{q}_2{}^2 + a_3 \dot{q}_3{}^2 + \ldots$$
$$V = b_1 q_1{}^2 + b_2 q_2{}^2 + b_3 q_3{}^2 + \ldots \quad \cdot \quad \cdot \quad (38)$$

The similarity between (37) and (38) is obvious. Further, it can be shown, though we shall not reproduce the analysis here, that Lagrange's equations of motion apply with the set of coordinates ϕ_r in just the same way as with the coordinates q_r in ordinary mechanics.

§ 23. We shall next discuss the normal modes of a string of length l when a mass M is tied to its mid-point (fig. 5). Now we have already seen in § 21 that in the

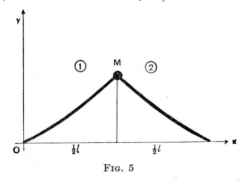

Fig. 5

normal vibrations of an unloaded string the normal modes of even order have a node at the mid-point. In such a vibration there is no motion at this point, and it is clearly irrelevant whether there is or is not a mass concentrated there. Accordingly, the normal modes of even order are unaffected by the presence of the mass, and our discussion will apply to the odd normal modes.

Just as in the calculations of §§ **16**, **17**, in which there was a discontinuity in the string, we shall have two separate expressions y_1 and y_2 valid in the regions $0 \leqslant x \leqslant l/2$ and $l/2 \leqslant x \leqslant l$. It is obvious that the two expressions must be such that y is symmetrical about the mid-point of the string. y_1 must vanish at $x = 0$ and y_2 at $x = l$. Consequently, we may try the solutions

$$y_1 = a \sin px \cos (cpt + \epsilon)$$
$$y_2 = a \sin p(l-x) \cos (cpt + \epsilon) \quad . \quad . \quad (39)$$

We have already satisfied the boundary condition $y_1 = y_2$ at $x = l/2$. There is still the other boundary condition which arises from the motion of M. Just as in (18) we may write this

$$F \left[\frac{\partial y_2}{\partial x} - \frac{\partial y_1}{\partial x} \right]_{x=l/2} = M \left[\frac{\partial^2 y_1}{\partial t^2} \right]_{x=l/2}.$$

Substituting the values of y_1 and y_2 as given by (39) and using the relation $F = c^2 \rho$, we find

$$\frac{pl}{2} \tan \frac{pl}{2} = \frac{\rho l}{M} = \text{const.} \quad . \quad . \quad (40)$$

The quantity $pl/2$ is therefore any one of the roots of the equation $x \tan x = \rho l/M$. If we draw the curves $y = \tan x$, $y = \rho l/Mx$, we can see that these roots lie in the regions 0 to $\pi/2$, π to $3\pi/2$, 2π to $5\pi/2$, etc. If we call the roots x_1, x_2 ... then the frequencies $cp/2\pi$ become $cx_r/\pi l$. If M is zero so that the string is unloaded, $x_r = (r+1/2)\pi$, so the presence of M has the effect of decreasing the frequencies of odd order.

If we write n for the frequency of a normal mode, then, since $n = cp/2\pi$, it follows that (40) can be written in the form of an equation to determine n directly ; viz.,

$$x \tan x = \rho l / M, \text{ where } x = (\pi l / c) n \qquad . \qquad (41)$$

This equation is called the **period equation.** Its solutions are the various permitted frequencies (and hence periods) of the normal modes. Period equations occur very frequently, especially when we have stationary type waves, and we shall often meet them in later chapters. This particular period equation is a transcendental equation with an infinite number of roots.

§ **24.** In the previous paragraphs we have assumed that there was no frictional resistance, so that the vibrations were undamped. In practice, however, the air does provide a resistance to motion ; this is roughly proportional to the velocity. Let us therefore discuss the motion of a string of length l fixed at its ends but subject to a resistance proportional to the velocity. The fundamental equation of wave motion (3) has to be supplemented by a term in $\dfrac{\partial y}{\partial t}$ and it becomes

$$\frac{\partial^2 y}{\partial x^2} = \frac{1}{c^2} \left\{ \frac{\partial^2 y}{\partial t^2} + k \frac{\partial y}{\partial t} \right\}. \qquad . \qquad . \qquad (42)$$

A solution by the method of separation of variables (cf. § **9**) is easily made, and we find

$$y = A e^{-\frac{1}{2}kt} \sin px \cos \left(\sqrt{(c^2 p^2 - k^2 / 4)}\, t + \epsilon\right).$$

Since y is to vanish at the two ends, we must have, as before, $\sin pl = 0$, and hence $p = r\pi / l$, $r = 1, 2, 3 \dots$. The normal modes of vibration are therefore

$$y = A_r e^{-\frac{1}{2}kt} \sin \frac{r\pi x}{l} \cos (qt + \epsilon_r) . \qquad . \qquad (43)$$

where

$$q^2 = \frac{r^2 \pi^2 c^2}{l^2} - \frac{k^2}{4}.$$

The exponential term $e^{-\frac{1}{2}kt}$ represents a decaying amplitude with modulus (see § **9**) equal to $2/k$. The frequency $q/2\pi$ is slightly less than when there is no frictional resistance. However, k is usually small, so that this decrease in frequency is often so small that it may be neglected.

§ **25.** There is another interesting method of obtaining the velocity of propagation of waves along a string, which we shall now describe and which is known as the method of **reduction to a steady wave.** Suppose that a wave is moving from left to right in fig. 6 with velocity c. Then,

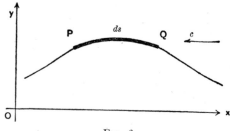

Fig. 6

if we superimpose on the whole motion a uniform velocity $-c$ the wave profile itself will be reduced to rest, and the string will everywhere be moving with velocity c, keeping all the time to a fixed curve (the wave profile). We are thus led to a different problem from our original one ; for now the string is moving and the wave profile is at rest, whereas originally the wave profile was moving and the string as a whole was at rest. Consider the motion of the small element PQ of length ds situated at the top of the hump of a wave. If R is the radius of curvature at this top point, and we suppose, as in § **13**, that the string is almost inextensible, then the acceleration of the element PQ is c^2/R downwards. Consequently, the forces acting on it must reduce to $(c^2/R)\,\rho ds$. But these forces are merely the two tensions F at P and Q, and just as in § **13** (especially note at foot of p. 23), they give a resultant $F ds/R$ downwards. Equating the two expressions, we have

$$\frac{c^2\rho}{R} ds = F \frac{ds}{R}, \text{ i.e. } c^2 = F/\rho.$$

This is, naturally, the same result as found before. The disadvantage of this method is that it does not describe in detail the propagation of the wave, nor does it deal with stationary waves, so that we cannot use it to get the equation of wave motion, etc. It is, however, very useful if we are only concerned with the wave velocity, and we shall see later that this simple artifice of reducing the wave to rest can be used in other problems as well.

§ 26. Examples

(1) Find the velocity of waves along a string whose density is 4 gms. per cm. when stretched to a tension 90000 dynes.

(2) A string of unlimited length is pulled into a harmonic shape $y = a \cos kx$, and at time $t = 0$ it is released. Show that if F is the tension and ρ the density of the string, its shape at any subsequent time t is $y = a \cos kx \cos kct$, where $c^2 = F/\rho$. Find the mean kinetic and potential energies per unit length of string.

(3) Find the reflection coefficient for two strings which are joined together and whose densities are 25 gms. per cm. and 9 gms. per cm.

(4) An infinite string lies along the x axis. At $t = 0$ that part of it between $x = \pm a$ is given a transverse velocity $a^2 - x^2$. Describe, with the help of equation (9) the subsequent motion of the string, the velocity of wave motion being c.

(5) Investigate the same problem as in question (4) except that the string is finite and of length $2a$, fastened at the points $x = \pm a$.

(6) What is the total energy of the various normal modes in question (5) ? Verify, by summation over all the normal modes, that this is equal to the initial kinetic energy.

(7) The two ends of a uniform stretched string are fastened to light rings that can slide freely on two fixed parallel wires $x = 0$, $x = l$, one ring being on each wire. Find the normal modes of vibration.

(8) A uniform string of length $3l$ fastened at its ends, is plucked a distance a at a point of trisection. It is then released from rest. Find the energy in each of the normal modes and verify that the sum is indeed equal to the work done in plucking the string originally.

(9) Discuss fully the period equation (41) in § 23. Show in particular that successive values of x approximate to $r\pi$, and that a closer approximation is $x = r\pi + \rho l/Mr\pi$.

(10) Show that the total energy of vibration (43) is
$$\tfrac{1}{4}\rho l A_r^2 e^{-kt}\{q^2 + kq \cos(qt+\epsilon_r)\sin(qt+\epsilon_r) + \tfrac{1}{2}k^2 \cos^2(qt+\epsilon_r)\},$$
and hence prove that the rate of dissipation of energy is
$$\tfrac{1}{8}k\rho l A_r^2 e^{-kt}\{2q \sin(qt+\epsilon_r) + k \cos(qt+\epsilon_r)\}^2.$$

(11) Two uniform wires of densities ρ_1 and ρ_2 and of equal length are fastened together at one end and the other two ends are tied to two fixed points a distance $2l$ apart. The tension is F. Find the normal periods of vibration.

(12) The density of a stretched string is m/x^2. The end-points are at $x = a$, $2a$, and the tension is F. Verify that the normal vibrations are given by the expression
$$y = A \sin\left[\theta \log_e (x/a)\right]\left(\frac{x}{a}\right)^{1/2}\frac{\cos}{\sin} pt, \text{ where } \theta^2 = \frac{mp^2}{F} - \frac{1}{4}.$$

Show that the period equation is $\theta \log_e 2 = n\pi, n = 1, 2, \ldots$.

(13) A heavy uniform chain of length l hangs freely from one end, and performs small lateral vibrations. Show that the normal vibrations are given by the expression
$$y = A J_0(2p\sqrt{\{x/g\}}) \cos(pt+\epsilon),$$
where J_0 represents Bessel's function (§ 7) of order zero, x being measured from the lower end.

Deduce that the period equation is $J_0(2p\sqrt{\{l/g\}}) = \mathbf{0}.$

[ANSWERS :

1. 150 cms./sec. ; 2. $\tfrac{1}{4}Fa^2k^2\sin^2 kct$, $\tfrac{1}{4}Fa^2k^2\cos^2 kct$; 3. $1/16$;

5. $y = \Sigma b_r \cos\dfrac{(r+\tfrac{1}{2})\pi x}{a} \sin\dfrac{(r+\tfrac{1}{2})\pi ct}{a}$, $b_r = (-1)^r 4a^3/(r+\tfrac{1}{2})^4\pi^4 c$;

6. $8\rho a^5/15$; 7. $y = a_r \cos\dfrac{r\pi x}{l}\cos\left(\dfrac{r\pi ct}{l}+\epsilon_r\right)$; 8. energy in rth

normal mode $= \dfrac{27c^2a^2\rho}{4l\pi^2r^2}\sin^2\dfrac{r\pi}{3}$; sum $= 3c^2a^2\rho/4l$; 11. $2\pi/p$

where $c_1 \tan(pl/c_1) = -c_2 \tan(pl/c_2)$, $c_1^2 = F/\rho_1$, $c_2^2 = F/\rho_2.$]

CHAPTER III

WAVES IN MEMBRANES

§ 27. The vibrations of a plane membrane stretched to a uniform tension T may be discussed in a manner very similar to that which we have used in Chapter II for strings. When we say that the tension is T we mean that if a line of unit length is drawn in the surface of the membrane, then the material on one side of this line

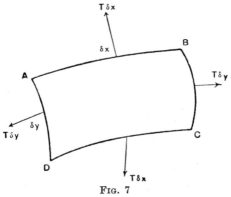

Fig. 7

exerts a force T on the material on the other side, and this force is perpendicular to the line we have drawn. Let us consider the vibrations of such a membrane ; we shall suppose that its thickness may be neglected. If its equilibrium position is taken as the xy plane, then we are concerned with displacements $z(xy)$ perpendicular to this plane. Consider a small rectangular element $ABCD$ (fig. 7) of sides δx, δy. When this is vibrating the forces on it are (a) two forces $\mathsf{T}\delta x$ perpendicular to AB and CD, and (b) two forces $\mathsf{T}\delta y$ perpendicular to AD and BC. These four forces act in the four tangent planes through the edges of the element. An argument precisely similar to that used in Chapter II, § **13**, shows that the forces (a) give a resultant $\mathsf{T}\delta x \cdot \dfrac{\partial^2 z}{\partial y^2} \delta y$ perpendicular to the plate. Similarly, the forces (b) reduce to a force $\mathsf{T}\delta y \cdot \dfrac{\partial^2 z}{\partial x^2} \delta x$. Let the mass of the plate be ρ per unit area : then, neglecting gravity, its equation of motion is

$$\mathsf{T} \frac{\partial^2 z}{\partial y^2} \delta x \delta y + \mathsf{T} \frac{\partial^2 z}{\partial x^2} \delta x \delta y = \rho \delta x \delta y \frac{\partial^2 z}{\partial t^2},$$

i.e.
$$\mathsf{T} \left\{ \frac{\partial^2 z}{\partial x^2} + \frac{\partial^2 z}{\partial y^2} \right\} = \rho \frac{\partial^2 z}{\partial t^2}.$$

This may be put in the standard form

$$\frac{\partial^2 z}{\partial x^2} + \frac{\partial^2 z}{\partial y^2} = \frac{1}{c^2} \frac{\partial^2 z}{\partial t^2}, \quad \cdot \quad \cdot \quad \cdot \quad (1)$$

where
$$c^2 = \mathsf{T}/\rho \quad \cdot \quad \cdot \quad \cdot \quad \cdot \quad (2)$$

Thus we have reduced our problem to the solution of the standard equation of wave motion, and shown that the velocity of waves along such membranes is $c = \sqrt{(\mathsf{T}/\rho)}$.

§ **28**. Let us apply these equations to a discussion of the transverse vibrations of a rectangular membrane $ABCD$ (fig. 8) of sides a and b. Take AB and AD as axes of x and y. Then we have to solve (1) subject to certain boundary conditions. These are that $z = 0$ at the boundary of the membrane, for all t. With our problem this means that $z = 0$ when $x = 0$, $x = a$, $y = 0$, $y = b$, independent of the time. The most suitable solution of the equation of wave motion is that of § **8**, equation (29). It is

$$z = \frac{\cos}{\sin} px \, \frac{\cos}{\sin} qy \, \frac{\cos}{\sin} rct \,, \quad p^2 + q^2 = r^2.$$

If z is to vanish at $x = 0$, $y = 0$, we shall have to reject the cosines in the first two factors. Further, if z vanishes

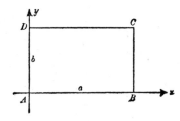

Fɪɢ. 8

at $x = a$, then $\sin pa = 0$, so that $p = m\pi/a$, and similarly $q = n\pi/b$, m and n being positive integers. Thus the normal modes of vibration may be written

$$z = A \sin \frac{m\pi x}{a} \sin \frac{n\pi y}{b} \cos (rct + \epsilon), \quad . \quad . \quad (3)$$

where
$$r^2 = (m^2/a^2 + n^2/b^2)\pi^2.$$

We may call this the (m, n) normal mode. Its frequency is $rc/2\pi$, i.e.

$$\sqrt{\left\{ \left(\frac{m^2}{a^2} + \frac{n^2}{b^2} \right) \frac{\mathsf{T}}{4\rho} \right\}} \quad . \quad . \quad . \quad (4)$$

The fundamental vibration is the $(1, 1)$ mode, for which the frequency is $\sqrt{\left\{ \left(\frac{1}{a^2} + \frac{1}{b^2} \right) \frac{\mathsf{T}}{4\rho} \right\}}$. The overtones (4) are not related in any simple numerical way to the fundamental, and for this reason the sound of a vibrating plate, in which as a rule several modes are excited together, is much less musical to the ear than a string, where the harmonics are all simply related to the fundamental.

In the (m, n) mode of (3) there are nodal lines $x = 0$, a/m, $2a/m$, ... a, and $y = 0$, b/n, $2b/n$, ... b. On opposite sides of any nodal line the displacement has opposite sign. A few normal modes are shown in fig. 9, in which the shaded parts are displaced oppositely to the unshaded.

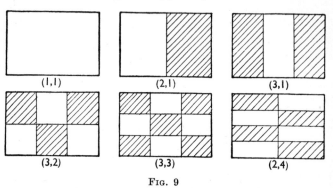

Fig. 9

The complete solution is the sum of any number of terms such as (3), with the constants chosen to give any assigned shape when $t = 0$. The method of choosing these constants is very similar to that of § **19**, except that there are now two variables x and y instead of one, and consequently we have double integrations corresponding to (27).

According to (4) the frequencies of vibration depend upon the two variables m and n. As a result it may happen that there are several different modes having the same frequency. Thus, for a square plate, the (4, 7), (7, 4), (1, 8) and (8, 1) modes have the same frequency; and for a plate for which $a = 3b$, the (3, 3) and (9, 1) modes have the same frequency. When we have two or more modes with the same frequency, we call it a **degenerate** case. It is clear that any linear combination of these modes gives another vibration with the same frequency.

§ 29. We can introduce normal coordinates as in the case of a vibrating string (cf. § 22). According to (3) the full expression for z is

$$z = \sum_{m, n} A_{mn} \cos (rct + \epsilon_r) \sin \frac{m\pi x}{a} \sin \frac{n\pi y}{b} \quad . \quad (5)$$

We write this

$$z = \sum_{m, n} \phi_{mn} \sin \frac{m\pi x}{a} \sin \frac{n\pi y}{b}, \quad . \quad . \quad (6)$$

where ϕ_{mn} are the normal coordinates. The kinetic energy is

$$\int\int \frac{1}{2} \rho \left(\frac{\partial z}{\partial t}\right)^2 dx\, dy, \quad . \quad . \quad . \quad (7)$$

and this is easily shown to be

$$T = \sum_{m, n} \frac{1}{8} \rho ab \dot{\phi}_{mn}^2 \quad . \quad . \quad . \quad (8)$$

The potential energy may be calculated in a manner similar to § 14. Referring to fig. 7 we see that in the displacement to the bent position, the two tensions $\mathsf{T}\delta y$ have done work $\mathsf{T}\delta y . (arc\, AB - \delta x)$. As in § 14, this reduces to approximately $\frac{1}{2} \mathsf{T} \left(\frac{\partial z}{\partial x}\right)^2 \delta x \delta y$. The other two tensions $\mathsf{T}\delta x$ have done work $\frac{1}{2} \mathsf{T} \left(\frac{\partial z}{\partial y}\right)^2 \delta x \delta y$. The total potential energy is therefore

$$V = \frac{1}{2} \mathsf{T} \int\int \left\{ \left(\frac{\partial z}{\partial x}\right)^2 + \left(\frac{\partial z}{\partial y}\right)^2 \right\} dx\, dy. \quad . \quad (9)$$

In the case of the rectangular membrane this reduces to

$$V = \sum_{m, n} \frac{1}{8} \rho abc^2 r^2 \phi_{mn}^2 \quad . \quad . \quad . \quad (10)$$

It will be seen that T and V are both expressed in the form of Chapter II, equation (38), typical of normal coordinates in mechanical problems.

§ **30.** With a circular membrane such as a drum of radius a, we have to use plane polar coordinates r, θ instead of Cartesians, and the solution of equation (1), apart from an arbitrary amplitude, is given in § **8**, equation (35a). It is

$$z = J_m(nr) \, {\cos \atop \sin} \, m\theta \cos nct.$$

We have neglected the $Y_m(nr)$ term since this is not finite at $r = 0$. If we choose the origin of θ properly, this normal mode may be written

$$z = J_m(nr) \cos m\theta \cos nct. \qquad . \qquad . \qquad (11)$$

If z is to be single-valued, m must be a positive integer. The boundary condition at $r = a$ is that for all values of θ and t, $J_m(na) \cos m\theta \cos nct$ equals zero. i.e., $J_m(na) = 0$. For any assigned value of m this equation has an infinite number of real roots, each one of which determines a corresponding value of n. These roots may be found from tables of Bessel functions. If we call them $n_{m,\,1}$, $n_{m,\,2}, \dots n_{m,\,k}, \dots$, then the frequency of (11) is $nc/2\pi$, i.e. $cn_{m,\,k}/2\pi$, and we may call it the (m, k) mode. The allowed values of m are 0, 1, 2, ... and of k are 1, 2, 3, ... There are nodal lines which consist of circles and radii vectores. Fig. 10 shows a few of these modes of vibration, shaded parts being displaced in an opposite direction to unshaded.

The nodal lines obtained in figs. 9 and 10 are known as Chladni's figures. A full solution of a vibrating membrane is obtained by superposing any number of these normal modes, and if nodal lines exist at all, they will not usually be of the simple patterns shown in these figures. As in the case of the rectangular membrane so also in the case of the circular membrane, the overtones bear no simple numerical relation to the fundamental frequency, and thus the sound of a drum is not very musical. A vibrating bell, however, is of very similar type, but it can be shown * that some of the more important overtones bear a simple numerical relation to the fundamental; this would explain the pleasant sound of a well-constructed bell. But it is a little difficult to see why the ear so readily rejects some of the other overtones

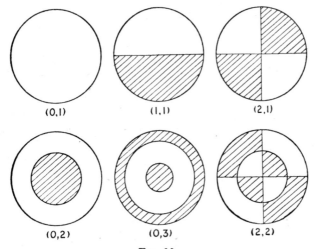

(0,1)   (1,1)   (2,1)

(0,2)   (0,3)   (2,2)

Fig. 10

whose frequencies are not simply related to the fundamental. A possible explanation † is that the mode of striking may be in some degree unfavourable to these discordant frequencies. In any case, we can easily understand why a bell whose shape differs slightly from the conventional, will usually sound unpleasant.

* See Slater and Frank, *Introduction to Theoretical Physics*, 1933, p. 161.
† Lamb, *Dynamical Theory of Sound* (Arnold), 1910, p. 155.

D

50 WAVES

§ 31.   Examples

(1) Find two normal modes which are degenerate (§ 28) for a rectangular membrane of sides 6 and 3.

(2) Obtain expressions for the kinetic and potential energies of a vibrating circular membrane. Perform the integrations over the θ-coordinate for the case of the normal mode

$$z = A J_m(nr) \cos m\theta \cos nct.$$

(3) A rectangular drum is 10 cm. $\times$ 20 cm. It is stretched to a tension of 5 kgm., and its mass is 20 gm. What is the fundamental frequency ?

(4) A square membrane bounded by $x = 0, a$ and $y = 0, a$ is distorted into the shape $z = A \sin \dfrac{2\pi x}{a} \sin \dfrac{3\pi y}{a}$ and then released. What is the resulting motion ?

(5) A rectangular membrane of sides a and b is stretched unevenly so that the tension in the x direction is T_1 and in the y direction is T_2. Show that the equation of motion is $T_1 \dfrac{\partial^2 z}{\partial x^2} + T_2 \dfrac{\partial^2 z}{\partial y^2} = \rho \dfrac{\partial^2 z}{\partial t^2}$. Show that this can be brought into the standard form by changing to new variables $x/\sqrt{T_1}$, $y/\sqrt{T_2}$, and hence find the normal modes.

(6) Show that the number of normal modes for the rectangular membrane of § 28 whose frequency is less than N is approximately equal to the area of a quadrant of the ellipse $\dfrac{x^2}{a^2} + \dfrac{y^2}{b^2} = \dfrac{4\rho}{T} N^2$. Hence show that the number is roughly $\pi \rho a b N^2/T$.

[ANSWERS: 1. $(2, 0)$ and $(0, 1)$: in general $(2m, n)$ and $(2n, m)$;   2. $T = \frac{1}{2}\pi \rho n^2 c^2 A^2 \sin^2 nct \int_0^a \{J_m(nr)\}^2 r\, dr,$

$V = \frac{1}{2}\pi \rho c^2 A^2 \cos^2 nct \int_0^a [n^2\{J_m'(nr)\}^2 + m^2\{J_m(nr)\}^2/r^2]\, r\, dr,$ which becomes, after integration by parts

$V = \frac{1}{2}\pi \rho n^2 c^2 A^2 \cos^2 nct \int_0^a \{J_m(nr)\}^2 r\, dr$; 3. $175\cdot1$ per sec.; 4. $z = A \sin (2\pi x/a) \sin (3\pi y/a) \cos (\sqrt{13}\pi ct/a)$; 5. $z = A \sin (m\pi x/a) \sin (n\pi y/b) \cos \pi pt,$
$$p^2 \rho = m^2 T_1/a^2 + n^2 T_2/b^2.]$$

CHAPTER IV

LONGITUDINAL WAVES IN BARS AND SPRINGS

§ 32. The vibrations which we have so far considered have all been transverse, so that the displacement has been perpendicular to the direction of wave propagation. We must now consider longitudinal waves, in which the displacement is in the same direction as the wave. Suppose that AB (fig. 11) is a bar of uniform section and

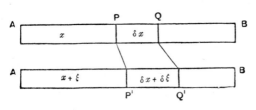

Fig. 11

mass ρ per unit length. The passage of a longitudinal wave along the bar will be represented by the vibrations of each element *along* the rod, instead of perpendicular to it. Consider a small element PQ of length δx, such that $AP = x$, and let us calculate the forces on this element, and hence its equation of motion, when it is displaced to a new position $P'Q'$. If the displacement of P to P' is ξ, then that of Q to Q' will be $\xi + \delta\xi$, so that $P'Q' = \delta x + \delta\xi$. We must first evaluate the tension at P'. We can do this by imagining δx to shrink to zero.

Then the infinitesimally small element around P' will be in a state of tension T where, by Hooke's Law,

$$\mathsf{T}_{P'} = \lambda \cdot \frac{\text{extension}}{\text{orig. length}}$$

$$= \lambda \lim_{\delta x \to 0} \frac{\delta x + \delta \xi - \delta x}{\delta x}$$

$$= \lambda \frac{\partial \xi}{\partial x} \qquad \cdot \qquad \cdot \qquad \cdot \qquad \cdot \qquad (1)$$

Returning to the element $P'Q'$, we see that its mass is the same as that of PQ, i.e. $\rho \delta x$, and its acceleration is $\frac{\partial^2 \xi}{\partial t^2}$. Therefore

$$\rho \delta x \cdot \frac{\partial^2 \xi}{\partial t^2} = \mathsf{T}_{Q'} - \mathsf{T}_{P'}$$

$$= \frac{\partial \mathsf{T}}{\partial x} \delta x = \lambda \frac{\partial^2 \xi}{\partial x^2} \delta x, \quad \text{by (1)}.$$

Thus the equation of motion for these longitudinal waves reduces to the usual equation of wave motion

$$\frac{\partial^2 \xi}{\partial x^2} = \frac{1}{c^2} \frac{\partial^2 \xi}{\partial t^2} \, , \quad \text{where } c^2 = \lambda/\rho \qquad \cdot \qquad (2)$$

The velocity of waves along a rod is therefore $\sqrt{(\lambda/\rho)}$, a result similar in form to the velocity of transverse oscillations of a string.

The full solution of (2) is soon found if we know the boundary conditions.

(i) At a free end the tension must vanish, and thus, from (1), $\frac{\partial \xi}{\partial x} = 0$, but the displacement will not, in general, vanish as well.

(ii) At a fixed end the displacement ξ must vanish, but the tension will not, in general, vanish also.

§ 33. If we are interested in the free vibrations of a bar of length l, we shall use stationary type solutions of (2) as in § 8, equation (27). Thus

$$\xi = (a \cos px + b \sin px) \cos \{cpt + \epsilon\}.$$

If we take the origin at one end, then by (i) $\partial\xi/\partial x$ has to vanish at $x = 0$ and $x = l$. This means that $b = 0$, and $\sin pl = 0$. i.e. $pl = n\pi$, where $n = 1, 2, \ldots$. The free modes are therefore described by the functions

$$\xi = a_n \cos \frac{n\pi x}{l} \cos \left\{ \frac{n\pi ct}{l} + \epsilon_n \right\} \quad . \qquad . \qquad (3)$$

This normal mode has frequency $nc/2l$, so that the fundamental frequency is $c/2l$, and the harmonics are simply related to it. There are nodes in (3) at the points $x = l/2n$, $3l/2n, 5l/2n, \ldots . (2n-1)l/2n$; and there are antinodes (§ 6) at $x = 0, 2l/2n, 4l/2n \ldots . l$. From (1) it follows that these positions are interchanged for the tension, nodes of motion being antinodes of tension and vice versa. We shall meet this phenomenon again in Chapter VI.

§ 34. The case of a rod rigidly clamped at its two ends is similarly solved. The boundary conditions are now that $\xi = 0$ at $x = 0$, and at $x = l$. The appropriate solution of (2) is thus

$$\xi = a_n \sin \frac{n\pi x}{l} \cos \left\{ \frac{n\pi ct}{l} + \epsilon_n \right\}. \quad . \qquad . \qquad (4)$$

This solution has the same form as that found in Chapter II, § 19, for the transverse vibrations of a string.

§ 35. We may introduce normal coordinates for these vibrations, just as in §§ 22 and 29. Taking, for example, the case of § 34, we should write

$$\xi = \sum_{n=1}^{\infty} \phi_n \sin \frac{n\pi x}{l}, \quad . \qquad . \qquad . \qquad (5)$$

where

$$\phi_n = a_n \cos \left\{ \frac{n\pi ct}{l} + \epsilon_n \right\}.$$

The kinetic energy of the element PQ is $\frac{1}{2}\rho\delta x . \dot{\xi}^2$, so that the total kinetic energy is

$$\int_0^l \frac{1}{2}\rho\dot{\xi}^2 dx = \sum_n \frac{1}{4}\rho l\dot{\phi}_n{}^2 \qquad . \qquad . \qquad . \qquad (6)$$

The potential energy stored up in $P'Q'$ is approximately equal to one-half of the tension multiplied by the increase in length : i.e. $\dfrac{1}{2}\lambda\dfrac{\partial\xi}{\partial x} . \partial\xi$. Thus the total potential energy is

$$\int_0^l \frac{1}{2}\lambda\left(\frac{\partial\xi}{\partial x}\right)^2 dx = \sum_n \frac{1}{4}\frac{\pi^2 n^2 c^2 \rho}{l}\phi_n{}^2 . \qquad . \qquad (7)$$

§ 36. The results of §§ 33, 34 for longitudinal vibrations of a bar need slight revision if the bar is initially in a state of tension. We shall discuss the vibrations of a bar of natural length l_0 stretched to a length l, so that its equilibrium tension T_0 is

$$T_0 = \lambda\frac{l - l_0}{l_0} \qquad . \qquad . \qquad . \qquad . \qquad (8)$$

Referring to fig. 11, we see that δx now represents the length of $P'Q'$ when in the stretched, non-vibrating state. The completely unstretched length is therefore not δx but $\dfrac{l_0}{l}\delta x$, so that the tension at P' is not given by (1), but by the modified relation

$$T_{P'} = \lambda \operatorname*{Lim}_{\delta x \to 0} \frac{\delta x + \delta\xi - \dfrac{l_0}{l}\delta x}{\dfrac{l_0}{l}\delta x}$$

$$= T_0 + \frac{\lambda l}{l_0}\frac{\partial\xi}{\partial x}, \text{ using (8)} . \qquad . \qquad (9)$$

The mass of PQ is $\rho_0(l_0/l)\delta x$ where ρ_0 refers to the unstretched bar, so the equation of motion is

$$\rho_0(l_0/l)\delta x \frac{\partial^2\xi}{\partial t^2} = T_{Q'} - T_{P'} = \frac{\partial T}{\partial x}\delta x$$

$$= \frac{\lambda l}{l_0}\frac{\partial^2\xi}{\partial x^2}\,\partial x \text{ from (9)}.$$

We have again arrived at the standard equation of wave motion

$$\frac{\partial^2 \xi}{\partial x^2} = \frac{1}{c^2} \frac{\partial^2 \xi}{\partial t^2} \ , \ \ c^2 = \lambda l^2 / \rho_0 l_0{}^2 \ . \qquad . \qquad (10)$$

It follows that $c = (l/l_0)c_0$, where c_0 is the velocity under no permanent tension. Appropriate solutions of (10) are soon seen to be

$$\xi = a_n \sin \frac{n\pi x}{l} \cos \left\{ \frac{n\pi ct}{l} + \epsilon_n \right\} \ , \ n = 1, 2 \ldots \qquad (11)$$

The fundamental frequency is $c/2l$, which, from (10), can be written $c_0/2l_0$. Thus with a given bar, the frequency is independent of the amount of stretching.

The normal mode (11) has nodes where $x = 0$, l/n, $2l/n, \ldots l$. A complete solution of (10) is obtained by superposition of separate solutions of type (11).

§ **37.** We shall conclude this chapter with a discussion of the vibrations of a spring suspended from its top end and carrying a load M at its bottom end. When we neglect the mass of the spring it is easy to show that the lower mass M (fig. 12) executes Simple Harmonic Motion in a vertical line. Let us, however, consider the possible vibrations when we allow for the mass m of the spring. Put $m = \rho l$, where ρ is the unstretched mass per unit length and l is the unstretched length. We may consider the spring in three stages. In stage (a) we have the unstretched spring of length l. The element PP' of length δx is at a distance x from the top point A. In stage (b) we have the equilibrium position when the spring is stretched due to its own weight and the load at the bottom. The element PP' is now displaced to QQ'. P is displaced a distance X downwards and P' a distance $X + \delta X$. Lastly, in stage (c) we suppose that the spring is vibrating and the element QQ' is displaced to RR'. The displacements of Q and Q' from their equilibrium positions are ξ and $\xi + \delta \xi$.

The new length RR' is therefore $\delta x + \delta X + \delta \xi$. The mass of the element is the same as the mass of PP', viz. $\rho \delta x$, and is of course the same in all three stages.

We are now in a position to determine the equation of motion of RR'. The forces acting on it are its weight

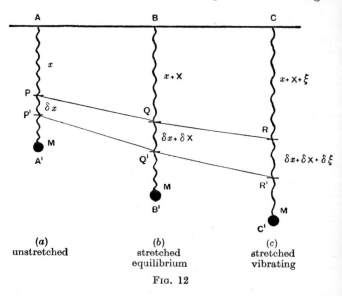

_(a)
unstretched

(b)
stretched
equilibrium

(c)
stretched
vibrating

Fig. 12

downwards and the two tensions at R and R'. The tension T_R may be found from Hooke's Law, by assuming that δx is made infinitesimally small. Then, as in § 36,

$$\mathsf{T}_R = \lambda \cdot \frac{\text{extension}}{\text{orig. length}}$$

$$= \lambda \, \underset{\delta x \to 0}{\text{Lim}} \, \frac{(\delta x + \delta X + \delta \xi) - \delta x}{\delta x}$$

$$= \lambda \left(\frac{\partial X}{\partial x} + \frac{\partial \xi}{\partial x} \right) \qquad . \qquad . \qquad . \qquad (12)$$

So the equation of motion of RR' is

$$\rho\delta x\,\frac{\partial^2 \xi}{\partial t^2} = \text{resultant force downwards}$$

$$= g\rho\delta x + \mathsf{T}_{R'} - \mathsf{T}_{R}\,,$$

$$= g\rho\delta x + \frac{\partial \mathsf{T}}{\partial x}\,\delta x.$$

Dividing by $\rho\delta x$ and using (12), this becomes

$$\frac{\partial^2 \xi}{\partial t^2} = g + \frac{\lambda}{\rho}\left(\frac{\partial^2 X}{\partial x^2} + \frac{\partial^2 \xi}{\partial x^2}\right).$$

This last equation must be satisfied by $\xi = 0$, since this is merely the position of equilibrium (b). So

$$0 = g + \frac{\lambda}{\rho}\frac{\partial^2 X}{\partial x^2}\,.$$

By subtraction we discover once more the standard equation of wave motion

$$\frac{\partial^2 \xi}{\partial x^2} = \frac{1}{c^2}\frac{\partial^2 \xi}{\partial t^2}\,,\quad c^2 = \frac{\lambda}{\rho} = \frac{\lambda l}{m} \qquad . \qquad . \qquad (13)$$

This result is very similar to that of § 36. However, before we can solve (13) we must discuss the boundary conditions. There are two of these. Firstly, when $x = 0$, we must have $\xi = 0$ for all t. Secondly, when $x = l$, (i.e. the position of the mass M) we must satisfy the law of motion

$$M\left[\frac{\partial^2 \xi}{\partial t^2}\right]_{x=l} = Mg - [\mathsf{T}]_{x=l}.$$

Using (12), this becomes

$$\left[\frac{\partial^2 \xi}{\partial t^2}\right]_{x=l} = g - \frac{\lambda}{M}\left[\frac{\partial X}{\partial x} + \frac{\partial \xi}{\partial x}\right]_{x=l}.$$

As before, this equation must be satisfied by $\xi = 0$, since this is just the equilibrium stage (b). Thus

$$0 = g - \frac{\lambda}{M}\left[\frac{\partial X}{\partial x}\right]_{x=l}.$$

So, by subtraction we obtain the final form of the second boundary condition

$$\left[\frac{\partial^2 \xi}{\partial t^2}\right]_{x=l} = -\frac{\lambda}{M}\left[\frac{\partial \xi}{\partial x}\right]_{x=l}. \qquad . \qquad (14)$$

The appropriate solution of (13) is

$$\xi = a \sin px \cos\{pct + \epsilon\}. \qquad . \qquad (15)$$

This gives $\xi = 0$ when $x = 0$, and therefore satisfies the first boundary condition. It also satisfies the other boundary condition (14) if

$$pl \tan pl = m/M. \qquad . \qquad . \qquad (16)$$

By plotting the curves $y = \tan x$, $y = (m/M)/x$, we see that there are solutions of (16) giving values of pl in the ranges 0 to $\pi/2$, π to $3\pi/2$, ... The solutions become progressively nearer to $n\pi$ as n increases.

We are generally interested in the fundamental, or lowest, frequency, since this represents the natural vibrations of M at the end of the spring. The harmonics represent standing waves in the spring itself, and may be excited by gently stroking the spring downwards when in stage (b). If m/M is small, the lowest root of (16) is small ; writing $pl = z$, we may expand $\tan z$ and get

$$z(z + z^3/3 + ...) = m/M.$$

Approximately

$$z^2(1 + z^2/3) = m/M.$$

We may put z^2 in the term in brackets equal to the first order approximation $z^2 = m/M$, and then we find for the second order approximation

$$z^2 = \frac{m/M}{1 + m/3M}.$$

The period of the lowest frequency in (15) is $2\pi/pc$, i.e., $2\pi l/cz$. Using the fact that $c^2 = \lambda l/m$, this becomes $2\pi\sqrt{\dfrac{l(M+\frac{1}{3}m)}{\lambda}}$. If the mass of the spring m had been neglected we should have obtained the result $2\pi\sqrt{(lM/\lambda)}$. It thus appears that the effect of the mass of the spring is equivalent, in a close approximation, to adding a mass one-third as great to the bottom of the spring.

§ 38.   Examples

(1) Find the velocity of longitudinal waves along a bar whose mass is $2 \cdot 25$ gms. per cm. and for which the modulus is $9 \cdot 0 \cdot 10^{10}$ dynes.

(2) Two semi-infinite bars are joined to form an infinite rod. Their moduli are λ_1 and λ_2 and the densities are ρ_1 and ρ_2. Investigate the reflection coefficient (see § 16) and the phase change on reflection, when harmonic waves in the first medium meet the join of the bars.

(3) Investigate the normal modes of a bar rigidly fastened at one end and free to move longitudinally at the other.

(4) A uniform bar of length l is hanging freely from one end. Show that the frequencies of the normal longitudinal vibrations are $(n+\frac{1}{2})\ c/2l$, where c is the velocity of longitudinal waves in the bar.

(5) The modulus of a spring is $7 \cdot 2 \cdot 10^3$ dynes. Its mass is 10 gms. and its unstretched length is 12 cms. A mass 40 gms. is hanging on the lowest point, and the top point is fixed. Calculate to an accuracy of 1 per cent. the periods of the lowest two vibrations.

(6) Investigate the vertical vibrations of a spring of unstretched length $2l$ and mass $2m$, supported at its top end and carrying loads M at the mid-point and the bottom.

[ANSWERS: 1. 2 km. per sec.; 2. $R = \left(\dfrac{\sqrt{(\lambda_1\rho_1)} - \sqrt{(\lambda_2\rho_2)}}{\sqrt{(\lambda_1\rho_1)} + \sqrt{(\lambda_2\rho_2)}}\right)^2$;

3. $\xi = A_r \sin \dfrac{(r+\frac{1}{2})\pi x}{l} \cos\left\{\dfrac{(r+\frac{1}{2})\pi ct}{l} + \epsilon_r\right\}$; 5. $1 \cdot 690$ secs., $0 \cdot 252$ secs.; 6. Period $= 2\pi/nc$ where $k^2 - 3k\cot nl + \cot^2 nl = 1$. $k = Mln/m$.]

CHAPTER V

WAVES IN LIQUIDS *

§ 39. In this chapter we shall discuss wave motion in liquids. We shall assume that the liquid is incompressible, with constant density ρ. This condition is very nearly satisfied by most liquids, and the case of a compressible fluid is dealt with in Chapter VI. We shall further assume that the motion is irrotational. This is equivalent to neglecting viscosity and assuming that all the motions have started from rest due to the influence of natural forces such as wind, gravity, or pressure of certain boundaries. If the motion is irrotational, we may assume the existence of a velocity potential ϕ if we desire it. It will be convenient to summarise the formulæ which we shall need in this work.

(i) If the vector $\mathbf{u}$ † with components $(u,\ v,\ w)$ ‡ represents the velocity of any part of the fluid, then from the definition of ϕ

$$\mathbf{u} = -\nabla\phi \equiv -\text{grad } \phi, \qquad . \quad . \quad (1)$$

so that in particular $u = -\partial\phi/\partial x$, $v = -\partial\phi/\partial y$, $w = -\partial\phi/\partial z$.

(ii) On a fixed boundary the velocity has no normal

---

* Before reading this chapter the student is advised to read Rutherford's *Vector Methods*, Chapter VI, from which several results will be quoted.

† Using Clarendon type for vectors.

‡ Many writers use $(u_x u_y u_z)$ for the velocity components. We shall find $(u,\ v,\ w)$ more convenient for our purposes. It is necessary, however, to distinguish $\mathbf{u}$, which is a vector representing the velocity and u, which is just the x component of the velocity.

component, and hence if $\partial/\partial\nu$ denotes differentiation along the normal

$$\partial\phi/\partial\nu = 0. \qquad . \qquad . \qquad . \qquad (2)$$

(iii) Since no liquid will be supposed to be created or annihilated, the equation of continuity must express the conservation of mass ; it is

$$\nabla . \mathbf{u} \equiv \frac{\partial u}{\partial x} + \frac{\partial v}{\partial y} + \frac{\partial w}{\partial z} = 0 \qquad . \qquad . \qquad (3)$$

Combining (1) and (3), we obtain Laplace's equation

$$\nabla^2\phi \equiv \frac{\partial^2\phi}{\partial x^2} + \frac{\partial^2\phi}{\partial y^2} + \frac{\partial^2\phi}{\partial z^2} = 0. \qquad . \qquad (4)$$

(iv) If $H(x, y, z, t)$ is any property of a particle of the fluid, such as its velocity, pressure or density, then $\dfrac{\partial H}{\partial t}$ is the variation of H at a *particular point in space*, and $\dfrac{DH}{Dt}$ is the variation of H *when we keep to the same particle of fluid*. $\dfrac{DH}{Dt}$ is known as the total differential coefficient, and it can be shown * that

$$\frac{DH}{Dt} = \frac{\partial H}{\partial t} + \mathbf{u} . \nabla H$$

i.e. $\qquad \dfrac{DH}{Dt} = \dfrac{\partial H}{\partial t} + u\dfrac{\partial H}{\partial x} + v\dfrac{\partial H}{\partial y} + w\dfrac{\partial H}{\partial z}.$ $\qquad (5)$

(v) If the external forces acting on unit mass of liquid can be represented by a vector $\mathbf{F}$, then the equation of motion of the liquid may be expressed in vector form

$$\frac{D\mathbf{u}}{Dt} = \mathbf{F} - \frac{1}{\rho}\nabla p.$$

* See Rutherford, § 66.

In Cartesian form this is

$$\frac{\partial u}{\partial t} + u\,\frac{\partial u}{\partial x} + v\,\frac{\partial u}{\partial y} + w\,\frac{\partial u}{\partial z} = F_x - \frac{1}{\rho}\frac{\partial p}{\partial x}, \quad . \quad (6)$$

with two similar equations for v and w.

(vi) An important integral of the equations of motion can be found in cases where the external force **F** has a potential V, so that $\mathbf{F} = -\nabla V$. The integral in question is known as Bernoulli's Equation:

$$\frac{p}{\rho} + \frac{1}{2}\mathbf{u}^2 + V - \frac{\partial \phi}{\partial t} = C, \quad . \quad . \quad (7)$$

where C is an arbitrary function of the time. Now according to (1), addition of a function of t to ϕ does not affect the velocity distribution given by ϕ; it is often convenient, therefore, to absorb C into the term $\dfrac{\partial \phi}{\partial t}$ and (7) can then be written

$$\frac{p}{\rho} + \frac{1}{2}\mathbf{u}^2 + V - \frac{\partial \phi}{\partial t} = \text{const.} \quad . \quad (8)$$

A particular illustration of (8) which we shall require later occurs at the surface of water waves; here the pressure must equal the atmospheric pressure and is hence constant. Thus at the surface of the waves (sometimes called the **free surface**)

$$\frac{1}{2}\mathbf{u}^2 + V - \frac{\partial \phi}{\partial t} = \text{constant.} \quad . \quad . \quad (9)$$

§ 40. We may divide the types of wave motion in liquids into two groups; the one group has been called **tidal waves,** * and arises when the wavelength of the oscillations is much greater than the depth of the liquid. Another name for these waves is **long waves in shallow water.** With waves of this type the vertical acceleration

* Lamb, *Hydrodynamics*, Chapter VIII.

of the liquid is neglected in comparison with the horizontal acceleration, and we shall be able to show that liquid originally in a vertical plane remains in a vertical plane throughout the vibrations; thus each plane of liquid moves as a whole. The second group may be called **surface waves**, and in these the disturbance does not extend far below the surface. The vertical acceleration is no longer negligible and the wavelength is much less than the depth of the liquid. To this group belong most wind waves and surface tension waves. We shall consider the two types separately, though it will be recognised that Tidal Waves represent an approximation and the results for these waves may often be obtained from the formulæ of Surface Waves by introducing certain restrictions.

TIDAL WAVES

§ **41.** We shall deal with Tidal Waves first. Here we assume that the vertical accelerations may be neglected. One important result follows immediately. If we draw the z axis vertically upwards (as we shall continue to do throughout this chapter), then the equation of motion in the z direction as given by (6), is

$$\frac{Dw}{Dt} = -g - \frac{1}{\rho}\frac{\partial p}{\partial z}.$$

We are to neglect $\dfrac{Dw}{Dt}$ and thus

$$\frac{\partial p}{\partial z} = -g\rho, \text{ i.e. } p = -g\rho z + \text{constant}.$$

Let us take our xy plane in the undisturbed free surface, and write $\zeta(x, y, t)$ for the elevation of the water above the point $(x, y, 0)$. Then, if the atmospheric pressure is p_0, we must have $p = p_0$ when $z = \zeta$. So the equation for the pressure becomes

$$p = p_0 + g\rho(\zeta - z). \quad . \quad . \quad . \quad (10)$$

We can put this value of p into the two equations of horizontal motion, and we obtain

$$\frac{Du}{Dt} = -g \frac{\partial \zeta}{\partial x} , \; \frac{Dv}{Dt} = -g \frac{\partial \zeta}{\partial y} . \quad . \quad (11)$$

The right-hand sides of these equations are independent of z, and we deduce therefore that in this type of motion the horizontal acceleration is the same at all depths. Consequently, as we stated earlier without proof, on still water the velocity does not vary with the depth, and the liquid moves as a whole, in such a way that particles originally in a vertical plane, remain so, although this vertical plane may move as a whole.

§ 42. Let us now apply the results of the last section to discuss tidal waves along a straight horizontal channel whose depth is constant, but whose cross-section A varies

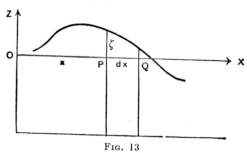

Fig. 13

from place to place. We shall suppose that the waves move in the x direction only (extension to two dimensions will come later). Consider the liquid in a small volume (fig. 13) bounded by the vertical planes x, $x+dx$ at P and Q. The liquid in the vertical plane through P is all moving with the same horizontal velocity $u(x)$ independent of the depth. We can suppose that A varies sufficiently slowly for us to neglect motion in the y direction. We have two equations with which to obtain the details of the motion. The first is (11) and may be written

$$\frac{\partial u}{\partial t} + u \frac{\partial u}{\partial x} + w \frac{\partial u}{\partial z} = -g \frac{\partial \zeta}{\partial x}.$$

Since u is independent of z, $\frac{\partial u}{\partial z} = 0$. Further, since we shall suppose that the velocity of any element of fluid is small, we may neglect $u \frac{\partial u}{\partial x}$ which is of the second order, and rewrite this equation

$$\frac{\partial u}{\partial t} = -g \frac{\partial \zeta}{\partial x} \qquad . \qquad . \qquad . \qquad (12)$$

The second equation is the equation of continuity. Equation (3) is not convenient for this problem, but a suitable equation can be found by considering the volume of liquid between the planes at P and Q, in fig. 13. Let $b(x)$ be the breadth of the water surface at P. Then the area of the plane P which is covered with water is $[A+b\zeta]_P$; therefore the amount of liquid flowing into the volume per unit time is $[(A+b\zeta)u]_P$. Similarly, the amount flowing out per unit time at Q is $[(A+b\zeta)u]_Q$. The difference between these is compensated by the rate at which the level is rising inside the volume, and thus

$$[(A+b\zeta)u]_P - [(A+b\zeta)u]_Q = b dx \frac{\partial \zeta}{\partial t}.$$

Therefore

$$-\frac{\partial}{\partial x} \{(A+b\zeta)u\} = b \frac{\partial \zeta}{\partial t}.$$

Since $b\zeta u$ is of the second order of small quantities, we may neglect this term and the equation of continuity becomes

$$-\frac{\partial}{\partial x} (Au) = b \frac{\partial \zeta}{\partial t} \qquad . \qquad . \qquad . \qquad (13)$$

E

Eliminating u between (12) and (13) gives us the equation

$$b \frac{\partial^2 \zeta}{\partial t^2} = \frac{\partial}{\partial x} \left(Ag \frac{\partial \zeta}{\partial x} \right). \qquad . \qquad . \qquad (14)$$

In the case in which A is constant, this reduces to the standard form

$$\frac{\partial^2 \zeta}{\partial x^2} = \frac{1}{c^2} \frac{\partial^2 \zeta}{\partial t^2}, \quad c^2 = Ag/b \qquad . \qquad . \qquad (15)$$

This is the familiar equation of wave motion in one dimension, and we deduce that waves travel with velocity $\sqrt{(Ag/b)}$. If the cross-section of the channel is rectangular, so that $A = bh$, h being the depth,

$$c = \sqrt{(gh)} \qquad . \qquad . \qquad . \qquad . \qquad (16)$$

With an unlimited channel, there are no boundary conditions involving x, and to our degree of approximation waves with any profile will travel in either direction. With a limited channel, there will be boundary conditions. Thus, if the ends are vertical, $u = 0$ at each of them.

We may apply this to a rectangular basin of length l, whose two ends are at $x = 0, l$. Possible solutions of (15) are given in § 8, equation (27). They are

$$\zeta = (a \cos px + \beta \sin px) \cos (cpt + \epsilon).$$

Then, using (13) and also the fact that $A = bh$, we find

$$\frac{\partial u}{\partial x} = \frac{cp}{h} (a \cos px + \beta \sin px) \sin (cpt + \epsilon).$$

$$\therefore \quad u = \frac{c}{h} (a \sin px - \beta \cos px) \sin (cpt + \epsilon).$$

The boundary conditions $u = 0$ at $x = 0, l$, imply that $\beta = 0$, and $\sin pl = 0$. So

$$\zeta = a_r \cos \frac{r \pi x}{l} \cos \left\{ \frac{r \pi c t}{l} + \epsilon_r \right\}, \; r = 1, 2, 3, \ldots \quad (17)$$

$$u = \frac{a_r c}{h} \sin \frac{r \pi x}{l} \sin \left\{ \frac{r \pi c t}{l} + \epsilon_r \right\} \qquad . \qquad . \qquad (18)$$

It will be noticed that nodes of u and ζ do not occur at the same points.

The vertical velocity may be found from the general form of the equation of continuity (3). Applied to our case, this is

$$\frac{\partial u}{\partial x} + \frac{\partial w}{\partial z} = 0.$$

Now u is independent of z and $w = 0$ on the bottom of the liquid where $z = -h$. Consequently, on integrating

$$w = -(z+h)\frac{\partial u}{\partial x} = \frac{-\pi r a_r c}{lh}(z+h)\cos\frac{r\pi x}{l}\sin\left\{\frac{r\pi ct}{l} + \epsilon_r\right\}. \quad (19)$$

We may use this last equation to deduce under what conditions our original assumption that the vertical acceleration could be neglected, is valid. For similarly to (12), the vertical acceleration $\dfrac{Dw}{Dt}$ is effectively $\dfrac{\partial w}{\partial t}$, i.e.

$$-\frac{\pi^2 r^2 c^2 a_r}{l^2 h}(z+h)\cos\frac{r\pi x}{l}\cos\left\{\frac{r\pi ct}{l} + \epsilon_r\right\}.$$

The maximum value of this is $\pi^2 r^2 c^2 a_r/l^2$, and may be compared with the maximum horizontal acceleration $\pi r c^2 a_r/lh$. The ratio of the two is $r\pi h/l$, i.e. $2\pi h/\lambda$, since, from (17) $\lambda = 2l/r$. We have therefore confirmed the condition which we stated as typical of these long waves, viz. that the vertical acceleration may be neglected if the wavelength is much greater than the depth of water.

§ 43. We shall now remove the restriction imposed in the last section to waves in one dimension. Let us use the same axes as before and consider the rate of flow of liquid into a vertical prism bounded by the planes x, $x+dx$, y, $y+dy$. In fig. 14, $ABCD$ is the undisturbed surface, $EFGH$ is the bottom of the liquid, and $PQRS$ is the moving surface at height ζ (x, y) above $ABCD$. The rate of flow into the prism across the face $PEHS$ is $[u(h+\zeta)dy]_x$, and the rate of flow out across $RQFG$ is $[u(h+\zeta)dy]_{x+dx}$. The net result from these two planes is

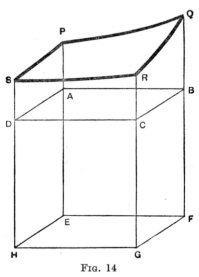

Fig. 14

a gain $-\dfrac{\partial}{\partial x}\{u(h+\zeta)\}dxdy$. Similarly, from the other two

vertical planes there is a gain $-\dfrac{\partial}{\partial y}\{v(h+\zeta)\}dxdy$. The

total gain is balanced by the rising of the level inside the prism, and thus

$$-\frac{\partial}{\partial x}\{u(h+\zeta)\}dxdy - \frac{\partial}{\partial y}\{v(h+\zeta)\}dxdy = \frac{\partial\zeta}{\partial t}\,.\,dxdy.$$

As in § 42, we may neglect terms such as $u\zeta$ and $v\zeta$ and write the above equation of continuity

$$\frac{\partial(hu)}{\partial x} + \frac{\partial(hv)}{\partial y} = -\frac{\partial\zeta}{\partial t}\,. \qquad . \qquad . \qquad (20)$$

We have to combine this equation with the two equations of motion (11), which yield, after neglecting square terms in the velocities

$$\frac{\partial u}{\partial t} = -g\frac{\partial \zeta}{\partial x}, \quad \frac{\partial v}{\partial t} = -g\frac{\partial \zeta}{\partial y} \quad . \quad . \quad (21)$$

Eliminating u and v gives us the standard equation

$$\frac{\partial}{\partial x}\left(h\frac{\partial \zeta}{\partial x}\right) + \frac{\partial}{\partial y}\left(h\frac{\partial \zeta}{\partial y}\right) = \frac{1}{g}\frac{\partial^2 \zeta}{\partial t^2} \quad . \quad . \quad (22)$$

If h is constant (tank of constant depth) this becomes

$$\frac{\partial^2 \zeta}{\partial x^2} + \frac{\partial^2 \zeta}{\partial y^2} = \frac{1}{c^2}\frac{\partial^2 \zeta}{\partial t^2}, \quad c^2 = gh \quad . \quad . \quad (23)$$

This is the usual equation of wave motion in two dimensions and shows that the velocity is $\sqrt{(gh)}$. If we are concerned with waves in one dimension, so that ζ is independent of y (as in § 42) we put $\frac{\partial^2 \zeta}{\partial y^2} = 0$ and retrieve (15).

We have therefore to solve the equation of wave motion subject to the boundary conditions

(i) $w = 0$ at $z = -h$,

(ii) $\frac{\partial \zeta}{\partial x} = 0$ at a boundary parallel to the y axis, and

$\frac{\partial \zeta}{\partial y} = 0$ at a boundary parallel to the x axis,

(iii) $\frac{\partial \zeta}{\partial \nu} = 0$ at any fixed boundary, where $\frac{\partial}{\partial \nu}$ denotes differentiation along the normal to the boundary. This latter condition, of which (ii) is a particular case, can be seen as follows. If $lx + my = 1$ is the fixed boundary, then the component of the velocity perpendicular to this line has to vanish. That is, $lu + mv = 0$. By differentiating partially with respect to t and using (21), the condition (iii) is obtained.

§ **44**. We shall apply these formulæ to two cases ; first, a rectangular tank, and, second, a circular one, both of constant depth.

Rectangular tank.—Let the sides be $x = 0, a$ and $y = 0, b$. Then a suitable solution of (23) satisfying all the boundary conditions (i) and (ii) would be

$$\zeta = A \cos \frac{p\pi x}{a} \cos \frac{q\pi y}{b} \cos (r\pi ct + \epsilon), \qquad (24)$$

where $p = 0, 1, 2 \dots, q = 0, 1, 2, \dots$, and $r^2 = p^2/a^2 + q^2/b^2$.

This solution closely resembles that for a vibrating membrane in Chapter III, § 28, and the nodal lines are of the same general type. The student will recognise how closely the solution (24) resembles a " choppy sea."

Circular tank.—If the centre of the tank is origin and its radius is a, then the boundary condition (iii) reduces to $\dfrac{\partial \zeta}{\partial r} = 0$ at $r = a$. Suitable solutions of (23) in polar coordinates have been given in Chapter I, equation (35a). We have

$$\zeta = A \cos m\theta \, J_m(nr) \cos (cnt + \epsilon) \qquad (25)$$

We have rejected the Y_m solution since it is infinite at $r = 0$, and we have chosen the zero of θ so that there is no term in $\sin m\theta$. This expression satisfies all the conditions except the boundary condition (iii) at $r = a$. This requires that $J_m'(na) = 0$. For a given value of m (which must be integral) this condition determines an infinite number of values of n, whose magnitudes may be found from tables of Bessel Functions. The nodal lines are concentric circles and radii from the origin, very similar to those in fig. 10 for a vibrating membrane. The period of this motion is $2\pi/cn$.

§ **45**. It is possible to determine the actual paths of individual particles in many of these problems. Thus, referring to the rectangular tank of § **42**, the velocities u and w are given by (18) and (19). We see that

$$\frac{w}{u} = \frac{-\pi r(z+h)}{l} \cot \frac{r\pi x}{l}.$$

This quantity is independent of the time and thus any particle of the liquid executes simple harmonic motion along a line whose slope is given by the above value of w/u. For particles at a fixed depth, this direction changes from purely horizontal beneath the nodes to purely vertical beneath the antinodes.

§ **46**. We shall conclude our discussion of tidal waves by applying the method of reduction to a steady wave, already described in § **25**, to the case of waves in a channel of constant cross-section A and breadth of water-line b. This is the problem of § **42** with A constant. Let c be the velocity of propagation of a wave profile. Then superimpose a velocity $-c$ on the whole system, so that the wave profile becomes stationary and the liquid flows under it with mean velocity c. The actual velocity at any point will differ from c since the cross-sectional area of the liquid is not constant. This area is $A+b\zeta$, and varies with ζ. Let the velocity be $c+\theta$ at sections where the elevation is ζ. Since no liquid is piling up, the volume of liquid crossing any plane perpendicular to the direction of flow is constant, i.e.

$$(A+b\zeta)(c+\theta) = \text{constant} = Ac. \qquad . \qquad (26)$$

We have still to use the fact that the pressure at the free surface is always atmospheric. In Bernouilli's equation at the free surface (9) we may put $\partial\phi/\partial t = 0$ since the motion is now steady motion; also $V = g\zeta$ at the free surface. So, neglecting squares of the vertical velocity, this gives

$$\tfrac{1}{2}(c+\theta)^2 + g\zeta = \text{const.} = \tfrac{1}{2}c^2.$$

Eliminating θ between this equation and (26), we have

$$\frac{A^2c^2}{(A+b\zeta)^2} + 2g\zeta = c^2,$$

i.e.

$$2g\zeta = c^2\left\{1 - \frac{A^2}{(A+b\zeta)^2}\right\} = bc^2\zeta\left[\frac{2A+b\zeta}{(A+b\zeta)^2}\right].$$

Whence

$$c^2 = \frac{2g}{b}\frac{(A+b\zeta)^2}{2A+b\zeta} \qquad . \qquad . \qquad . \qquad (27)$$

If ζ is small, so that we may neglect ζ compared with A/b, then this equation gives the same result as (16), viz. $c^2 = gA/b$. We can, however, deduce more than this simple result. For if $\zeta > 0$, the right-hand side of (27) is greater than gA/b, and if $\zeta < 0$, it is less than gA/b. Thus an elevation travels slightly faster than a depression and so it is impossible for a long wave to be propagated without change of shape. Further, since the tops of waves travel faster than the troughs, we have an explanation of why waves break on the sea-shore when they reach shallow water.

SURFACE WAVES

§ 47. We now consider Surface Waves, in which the restriction is removed that the wavelength is much greater than the depth. In these waves the disturbance is only appreciable over a finite depth of the liquid. We shall solve this problem by means of the velocity potential ϕ. ϕ must satisfy Laplace's equation (4) and at any fixed boundary $\partial\phi/\partial\nu = 0$, by (2). There are, however, two other conditions imposed on ϕ at the free surface. The first arises from Bernoulli's equation (9). If the velocity is so small that $\mathbf{u}^2$ may be neglected, and if the only external forces are the external pressure and gravity, we may put $\mathbf{u}^2 = 0$ and $V = g\zeta$ in this equation, which becomes

$$\zeta = \frac{1}{g}\left[\frac{\partial\phi}{\partial t}\right]_{\text{free surface}} \qquad . \qquad . \qquad (28)$$

The second condition can be seen as follows. A particle of fluid originally on the free surface will remain so always. Now the equation of the free surface, where $z = \zeta(x, y, t)$ may be written

$$0 = f(x, y, z, t) = \zeta(x, y, t) - z.$$

Consequently, f is a function which is always zero *for a particle on the free surface*. We may therefore use (5) with H put equal to f, and we find

$$0 = \frac{Df}{Dt} = \frac{\partial\zeta}{\partial t} + u\frac{\partial\zeta}{\partial x} + v\frac{\partial\zeta}{\partial y} - w.$$

Now from (28) $\dfrac{\partial\zeta}{\partial x} = \dfrac{1}{g}\dfrac{\partial}{\partial t}\left(\dfrac{\partial\phi}{\partial x}\right) = -\dfrac{1}{g}\dfrac{\partial u}{\partial t}$ on the surface.

Thus $\dfrac{\partial\zeta}{\partial x}$ is a small quantity of order of magnitude not greater than u; consequently $u\dfrac{\partial\zeta}{\partial x}$ and $v\dfrac{\partial\zeta}{\partial y}$, being of order of magnitude not greater than u^2, may be neglected. We are left with the new boundary condition

$$\frac{\partial\zeta}{\partial t} = w = -\frac{\partial\phi}{\partial z} \qquad . \qquad . \qquad . \qquad (29)$$

Combining (28) and (29) we obtain an alternative relation

$$\frac{\partial^2\phi}{\partial t^2} + g\frac{\partial\phi}{\partial z} = 0 \qquad . \qquad . \qquad . \qquad (30)$$

We summarise the conditions satisfied by ϕ as follows :

    (i) Laplace's equation $\nabla^2\phi = 0$ in the liquid .   (4)

    (ii) $\partial\phi/\partial\nu = 0$ on a fixed boundary .   .   .   (2)

(iii) $\quad \zeta = \dfrac{1}{g}\dfrac{\partial \phi}{\partial t}$ on the free surface . . . (28)

(iv) $\quad \dfrac{\partial \zeta}{\partial t} = -\dfrac{\partial \phi}{\partial z}$ on the free surface . . . (29)

(v) $\quad \dfrac{\partial^2 \phi}{\partial t^2} + g\dfrac{\partial \phi}{\partial z} = 0$ on the free surface . . (30)

Only two of the last three conditions are independent.

§ 48. Let us apply these equations to the case of a liquid of depth h in an infinitely long rectangular tank, supposing that the motion takes place along the length of the tank, which we take as the x direction. The axes of x and y lie, as usual, in the undisturbed free surface. Condition (i) above gives an equation which may be solved by the method of separation of variables (see § 7), and if we want our solution to represent a progressive wave with velocity c, a suitable form of the solution would be

$$\phi = (Ae^{mz} + Be^{-mz})\cos m(x-ct).$$

A, B, m and c are to be determined from the other conditions (ii)-(v). At the bottom of the tank (ii) gives $\partial \phi/\partial z = 0$, i.e. $Ae^{-mh} - Be^{mh} = 0$. So $Ae^{-mh} = Be^{mh} = \frac{1}{2}C$, say, and hence

$$\phi = C\cosh m(z+h)\cos m(x-ct). \qquad . \qquad (31)$$

Condition (v) applies at the free surface where, if the disturbance is not too large, we may put $z = 0$; after some reduction it becomes

$$c^2 = (g/m)\tanh mh.$$

Since $m = 2\pi/\lambda$, where λ is the wavelength, we can write this

$$c^2 = \frac{g\lambda}{2\pi}\tanh\frac{2\pi h}{\lambda} \qquad . \qquad . \qquad . \qquad (32)$$

Condition (iii) gives us the appropriate form of ζ; it is

$$\zeta = \frac{mcC}{g} \cosh mh \sin m(x-ct).$$

This expression becomes more convenient if we write a for the amplitude of ζ; i.e., $a = \dfrac{mcC}{g} \cosh mh$. Then

$$\zeta = a \sin m(x-ct), \qquad \cdot \quad \cdot \quad \cdot \quad \cdot \quad (33)$$

$$\phi = \frac{ga}{mc} \frac{\cosh m(z+h)}{\cosh mh} \cos m(x-ct). \qquad \cdot \quad (34)$$

If the water is very deep so that $\tanh (2\pi h/\lambda) = 1$, then (32) becomes $c^2 = g\lambda/2\pi$, and if it is very shallow so that $\tanh (2\pi h/\lambda) = 2\pi h/\lambda$, we retrieve the formula of § 42 for long waves in shallow water, viz. $c^2 = gh$.

We have seen in Chapter I that stationary waves result from superposition of two opposite progressive harmonic waves. Thus we could have stationary waves analogous to (33) and (34) defined by

$$\zeta = a \sin mx \cos mct, \qquad \cdot \quad \cdot \quad \cdot \quad \cdot \quad (35)$$

$$\phi = \frac{ga}{mc} \frac{\cosh m(z+h)}{\cosh mh} \sin mx \sin mct. \qquad \cdot \quad (36)$$

We could use these last two equations to discuss stationary waves in a rectangular tank of finite length.

§ 49. We shall now discuss surface waves in two dimensions, considering two cases in particular.

Rectangular tank.—With a rectangular tank bounded by the planes $x = 0, a$ and $y = 0, b$, it is easily verified that all the conditions of § 47 are satisfied by

$$\zeta = A \cos \frac{p\pi x}{a} \cos \frac{q\pi y}{b} \cos rct,$$

$$\phi = \frac{gA}{rc} \frac{\cosh r(z+h)}{\cosh rh} \cos \frac{p\pi x}{a} \cos \frac{q\pi y}{b} \sin rct,$$

where

$$p = 1, 2, \ldots ; \quad q = 1, 2, \ldots ; \quad r^2 = \pi^2(p^2/a^2 + q^2/b^2) \text{ and}$$
$$c^2 = (g/r) \tanh rh. \qquad . \qquad . \qquad . \qquad (37)$$

Circular tank.—Suppose that the tank is of radius a and depth h. Then choosing the centre as origin and using cylindrical polar coordinates r, θ, z, Laplace's equation (cf. Chapter I, § 7) becomes

$$\frac{\partial^2 \phi}{\partial r^2} + \frac{1}{r} \frac{\partial \phi}{\partial r} + \frac{1}{r^2} \frac{\partial^2 \phi}{\partial \theta^2} + \frac{\partial^2 \phi}{\partial z^2} = 0 \qquad . \qquad (38)$$

A suitable solution can be found from Chapter I, equation (35a), which gives us a solution of the similar equation

$$\frac{\partial^2 \phi}{\partial r^2} + \frac{1}{r} \frac{\partial \phi}{\partial r} + \frac{1}{r^2} \frac{\partial^2 \phi}{\partial \theta^2} - \frac{1}{c^2} \frac{\partial^2 \phi}{\partial t^2} = 0$$

in the form

$$\phi = \frac{J_m}{Y_m}(nr) \frac{\cos}{\sin} m\theta \frac{\cos}{\sin} nct.$$

In this equation let us make a change of variable, writing $ct = iz$, where $i^2 = -1$. We then get Laplace's equation (38) and its solutions are therefore

$$\phi = \frac{J_m}{Y_m}(nr) \frac{\cos}{\sin} m\theta \frac{\cosh}{\sinh} nz , \quad m = 0, 1, 2, \ldots .$$

In our problem we must discard the Y solution as $Y_m(r)$ is infinite when $r = 0$. So, choosing our zero of θ suitably, we can write

$$\phi = J_m(nr) \cos m\theta \, (A \cosh nz + B \sinh nz).$$

At the bottom of the tank condition (ii) gives, as in § 48, $A \sinh nh = B \cosh nh$, so that

$$\phi = C J_m(nr) \cos m\theta \cosh n(z + h).$$

The constants m and n are not independent, since we have to satisfy the boundary condition at $r = a$. This gives $J_m'(na) = 0$, so that for any selected m, n is restricted to have one of a certain set of values, determined from the roots of the above equation. The function C above will involve the time, and in fact if we are interested in waves whose frequency is f, we shall try $C \propto \sin 2\pi ft$. Putting $C = D \sin 2\pi ft$, where D is now a constant independent of r, θ, z or t, we have

$$\phi = D J_m(nr) \cos m\theta \cosh n(z+h) \sin 2\pi ft. \qquad (39)$$

The boundary condition § 47 (iii) now enables us to find ζ; it is

$$\zeta = \frac{2\pi Df}{g} J_m(nr) \cos m\theta \cosh nh \cos 2\pi ft \quad . \qquad (40)$$

The remaining boundary condition § 47 (iv) gives us the period equation; it is

$$-4\pi^2 f^2 D J_m(nr) \cos m\theta \cosh nh \sin 2\pi ft$$

$$+gnD J_m(nr) \cos m\theta \sinh nh \sin 2\pi ft = 0.$$

i.e. $$4\pi^2 f^2 = gn \tanh nh. \qquad . \qquad . \qquad . \qquad (41)$$

For waves with a selected value of m (which must be integral) n is found and hence, from (41) f is found. We conclude that only certain frequencies are allowed. Apart from an arbitrary multiplying constant, the nature of the waves is now completely determined.

§ 50. In § 48 we discussed the progressive wave motion in an infinite straight channel. It is possible to determine from (34) the actual paths of the particles of fluid in this motion. For if X, Z denote the displacements of a particle whose mean position is (x, z) we have

$$\dot{X} = -\frac{\partial \phi}{\partial x} = \frac{ga}{c} \frac{\cosh m(z+h)}{\cosh mh} \sin m(x-ct),$$

$$\dot{Z} = -\frac{\partial \phi}{\partial z} = -\frac{ga}{c} \frac{\sinh m(z+h)}{\cosh mh} \cos m(x-ct),$$

in which we have neglected terms of the second order of small quantities. Thus

$$X = \frac{ga \cosh m(z+h)}{mc^2 \cosh mh} \cos m(x-ct),$$

$$Z = \frac{ga \sinh m(z+h)}{mc^2 \cosh mh} \sin m(x-ct).$$

Eliminating t, we find for the required path

$$\frac{X^2}{\cosh^2 m(z+h)} + \frac{Z^2}{\sinh^2 m(z+h)} = \frac{g^2a^2}{m^2c^4 \cosh^2 mh}. \quad (42)$$

These paths are ellipses in a vertical plane with a constant distance $(2ga/mc^2)$ sech mh between their foci. A similar discussion could be given for the other types of wave motion which we have solved in other paragraphs.

§ 51. The Kinetic and Potential energies of these waves are easily determined. Thus, if we measure the P.E. relative to the undisturbed state, then, since $\zeta(x, y)$ is the elevation, the mass of liquid standing above a base dA in the xy plane is $\rho\zeta \, dA$. Its centre of mass is at a height $\frac{1}{2}\zeta$, and thus the total P.E. is

$$\int \tfrac{1}{2} g\rho\zeta^2 dA, \quad \cdot \quad \cdot \quad \cdot \quad \cdot \quad (43)$$

the integral being taken over the undisturbed area of surface. Likewise the K.E. of a small element is $\frac{1}{2}\rho\mathbf{u}^2 \, d\tau$, $d\tau$ being the element of volume of the liquid, so that the total K.E. is

$$T = \int \tfrac{1}{2}\rho\mathbf{u}^2 d\tau, \quad \cdot \quad \cdot \quad \cdot \quad (44)$$

the integral being taken over the whole liquid, which may, within our approximation, be taken to be the undisturbed volume.

With the progressive waves of § **48**, ζ and ϕ are given

by (33) and (34), and a simple integration shows that the
K.E. and P.E. in one wavelength $(2\pi/m)$ are equal, and
per unit width of stream, have the value

$$\tfrac{1}{4}g\rho a^2\lambda \quad . \quad . \quad . \quad . \quad . \quad (45)$$

In evaluating (44) it is often convenient to use Green's
Theorem in the form *

$$\int\left\{\left(\frac{\partial\phi}{\partial x}\right)^2 + \left(\frac{\partial\phi}{\partial y}\right)^2 + \left(\frac{\partial\phi}{\partial z}\right)^2\right\}d\tau = \int\phi\,\frac{\partial\phi}{\partial\nu}\,dS.$$

The latter integral is taken over the surface S which
bounds the original volume, and $\partial/\partial\nu$ represents differentiation along the outward normal to this volume.   Since
$\partial\phi/\partial\nu = 0$ on a fixed boundary, some of the contributions
to T will generally vanish.   Also, on the free surface, if
ζ is small, we may put $\partial\phi/\partial z$ instead of $\partial\phi/\partial\nu$.

§ 52. We shall next calculate the rate at which energy
is transmitted in one of these surface waves.   We can

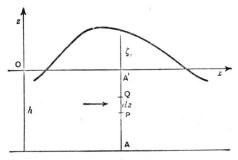

Fɪɢ. 15.

illustrate the method by considering the problem discussed
in § 48, i.e. progressive waves in a rectangular tank of
depth h.   Let AA' (fig. 15) be an imaginary plane fixed
in the liquid perpendicular to the direction of wave

* See Rutherford, Chapter VI, p. 66 (ii).

propagation. We shall calculate the rate at which the liquid on the left of AA' is doing work upon the liquid on the right. This will represent the rate at which the energy is being transmitted. Suppose that the tank is of unit width and consider that part of AA' which lies between the two lines z, $z+dz$ (shown as PQ in the figure). At all points of this area the pressure is p, and the velocity is u. The rate at which work is being done is therefore $pudz$. Thus the total rate is $\int_{-h}^{0} pudz$. We use Bernoulli's equation (8) to give us p; since $\mathbf{u}^2$ may be neglected, and $V = gz$, therefore

$$p = p_0 + \rho\frac{\partial\phi}{\partial t} - g\rho z.$$

Now, according to (1) $u = -\partial\phi/\partial x$ and from (34),

$$\phi = \frac{ga}{mc}\frac{\cosh m(z+h)}{\cosh mh}\cos m(x-ct).$$

Putting these various values in the required integral we obtain

$$\sin m(x-ct)\int_{-h}^{0}\frac{ga}{c}\frac{\cosh m(z+h)}{\cosh mh}(p_0 - g\rho z)dz$$

$$+ \sin^2 m(x-ct)\int_{-h}^{0}\frac{\rho g^2 a^2}{c}\frac{\cosh^2 m(z+h)}{\cosh^2 mh}dz.$$

This expression fluctuates with the time, and we are concerned with its mean value. The mean value of $\sin m(x-ct)$ is zero, and of $\sin^2 m(x-ct)$ is $\frac{1}{2}$. Thus the mean rate at which work is being done is

$$\frac{\rho g^2 a^2}{2c}\operatorname{sech}^2 mh\int_{-h}^{0}\cosh^2 m(z+h)dz.$$

After some reduction this becomes

$$\tfrac{1}{4}g\rho a^2 c\,(1 + 2mh\operatorname{cosech} 2mh).$$

In terms of the wavelength $\lambda = 2\pi/m$, this is

$$\frac{1}{4} g\rho a^2 c \left\{ 1 + \frac{4\pi h}{\lambda} \operatorname{cosech} \frac{4\pi h}{\lambda} \right\} \qquad . \qquad . \qquad (46)$$

Now from (45) we see that the total energy with a stream of unit width is $\frac{1}{2} g\rho a^2$ per unit length. Thus the velocity of energy flow is

$$\frac{c}{2} \left\{ 1 + \frac{4\pi h}{\lambda} \operatorname{cosech} \frac{4\pi h}{\lambda} \right\} \qquad . \qquad . \qquad (47)$$

We shall see in a later chapter that this velocity is an important quantity known as the Group Velocity.

§ 53. In the preceding paragraphs we have assumed that surface tension could be neglected. However, with short waves this is not satisfactory and we must now investigate the effect of allowing for it. When we say that the surface tension is T, we mean that if a line of unit length is drawn in the surface of the liquid, then the liquid on one side of this line exerts a pull on the liquid on the other side, of magnitude T. Thus the effect of Surface Tension is similar to that of a membrane everywhere stretched to a tension T (as in Chapter III, § 27), placed on the surface of the liquid. We showed in Chapter III that when the membrane was bent there was a downward force per unit area approximately equal to $-\mathsf{T}\left\{\dfrac{\partial^2 \zeta}{\partial x^2} + \dfrac{\partial^2 \zeta}{\partial y^2}\right\}$. Thus in fig. 16, the pressure p_1 *just inside* the liquid does not equal the atmospheric pressure p_0, but rather

$$p_1 = p_0 - \mathsf{T} \left\{ \frac{\partial^2 \zeta}{\partial x^2} + \frac{\partial^2 \zeta}{\partial y^2} \right\} \qquad . \qquad . \qquad (48)$$

The reader who is familiar with hydrostatics will recognise that the excess pressure inside a stretched film (as in a soap bubble) is $\mathsf{T}(1/R_1 + 1/R_2)$, where R_1 and R_2 are the radii of curvature in any pair of perpendicular

F

planes through the normal to the surface. We may put $R_1 = -\partial^2\zeta/\partial x^2$ and $R_2 = -\partial^2\zeta/\partial y^2$ to the first order of small quantities, and then (48) follows immediately.

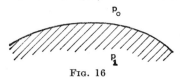

Fig. 16

Thus, instead of being $p = p_0$ at the free surface of the liquid, the correct condition is that $p + \mathsf{T}\left\{\dfrac{\partial^2\zeta}{\partial x^2} + \dfrac{\partial^2\zeta}{\partial y^2}\right\}$ is constant and equal to p_0. We may combine this with Bernoulli's equation (9), in which we neglect $\mathbf{u}^2$ and put $V = gz$. Then the new boundary condition which replaces § 47 (iii) is

$$\frac{\partial\phi}{\partial t} - g\zeta + \frac{\mathsf{T}}{\rho}\left\{\frac{\partial^2\zeta}{\partial x^2} + \frac{\partial^2\zeta}{\partial y^2}\right\} = 0 \qquad . \qquad (49)$$

We still have the boundary condition § 47 (iv) holding, since this is not affected by any sudden change in pressure at the surface. By combining (29) and (49) we find the new condition that replaces § 47 (v). It is

$$\frac{\partial^2\phi}{\partial t^2} + g\frac{\partial\phi}{\partial z} - \frac{\mathsf{T}}{\rho}\left\{\frac{\partial^2}{\partial x^2} + \frac{\partial^2}{\partial y^2}\right\}\frac{\partial\phi}{\partial z} = 0 \qquad . \qquad (50)$$

We may collect these formulæ together ; thus, with surface tension

(i) $\nabla^2\phi = 0$ in the body of the liquid . . (4)

(ii) $\partial\phi/\partial\nu = 0$ on all fixed boundaries . . (2)

(iii) $\dfrac{\partial\phi}{\partial t} - g\zeta + \dfrac{\mathsf{T}}{\rho}\left\{\dfrac{\partial^2\zeta}{\partial x^2} + \dfrac{\partial^2\zeta}{\partial y^2}\right\} = 0$ on the free surface (49)

(iv) $\partial\zeta/\partial t = -\partial\phi/\partial z$ on the free surface . . (29)

(v) $\dfrac{\partial^2\phi}{\partial t^2} + g\dfrac{\partial\phi}{\partial z} - \dfrac{\mathsf{T}}{\rho}\left\{\dfrac{\partial^2}{\partial x^2} + \dfrac{\partial^2}{\partial y^2}\right\}\dfrac{\partial\phi}{\partial z} = 0$ on the free surface . (50)

Only two of the last three equations are independent.

§ 54. Waves of the kind in which surface tension is important are known as **capillary waves**. We shall discuss one case which will illustrate the conditions (i)-(v). Let us consider progressive type waves on an unlimited sheet of water of depth h, assuming that the motion takes place exclusively in the direction of x. Then, by analogy with (31) we shall try

$$\phi = C \cosh m(z+h) \cos m(x-ct). \quad . \quad . \quad (51)$$

This satisfies (i) and (ii). (iv) gives the form of ζ, which is

$$\zeta = (C/c) \sinh mh \sin m(x-ct). \quad . \quad . \quad (52)$$

We have only one more condition to satisfy; if we choose (v) this gives

$$-m^2c^2C \cosh mh \cos m(x-ct)+mCg \sinh mh \cos m(x-ct)$$

$$+ \frac{\mathsf{T}}{\rho} m^3C \sinh mh \cos m(x-ct) = 0,$$

i.e. $\qquad c^2 = (g/m+\mathsf{T}m/\rho) \tanh mh. \quad . \quad . \quad (53)$

This equation is really the modified version of (32) when allowance is made for the surface tension; if $\mathsf{T} = 0$, it reduces to (32).

When h is large, $\tanh mh = 1$, and if we write $m = 2\pi/\lambda$, we have

$$c^2 = \frac{g\lambda}{2\pi} + \frac{2\pi\mathsf{T}}{\lambda\rho}. \quad . \quad . \quad . \quad (54)$$

The curve of c against λ is shown in fig. 17, from which it can be seen that there is a minimum velocity which occurs when $\lambda^2 = 4\pi^2\mathsf{T}/g\rho$. Waves shorter than this, in which surface tension is dominant, are called **ripples**, and it is seen that for any velocity greater than the minimum there are two possible types of progressive wave, one of which is a ripple. The minimum velocity is $(4g\mathsf{T}/\rho)^{1/4}$, and if, as in water, $\mathsf{T} = 75$, $\rho = 1{\cdot}00$ and $g = 981$ c.g.s. units, this critical velocity is about 23 cms. per sec., and the critical wavelength is about 17 cms. Curves of c against λ for other values of the depth h are very similar to fig. 17.

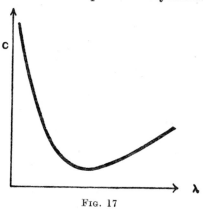

Fig. 17

§ 55. Examples

(1) Find the Potential and Kinetic energies for tidal waves in a tank of length l, using the notation of § 42.

(2) Find the velocity of any particle of liquid in the problem of tidal waves in a circular tank of radius a (§ 44). Show that when $m = 0$ in (25), particles originally on a vertical cylinder of radius r coaxial with the tank, remain on a coaxial cylinder whose radius fluctuates; find an expression for the amplitude of oscillation of this radius in terms of r.

(3) Tidal waves are occurring in a square tank of depth h and side a. Find the normal modes, and calculate the Kinetic and Potential energies for each of them. Show that when more than one such mode is present, the total energy is just the sum of the separate energies of each normal mode.

(4) What are the paths of the particles of the fluid in the preceding question?

(5) A channel of unit width is of depth h, where $h = kx$, k being a constant. Show that tidal waves are possible with frequency $p/2\pi$, for which

$$\zeta = A J_0(a x^{1/2}) \cos pt,$$

where $a^2 = 4p^2/kg$, and J_0 is Bessel's function of order zero. It is known that the distance between successive zeros of $J_0(x)$ tends to π when x is large. Hence show that the wavelength of these stationary waves increases with increasing values of x (This is the problem of a shelving beach.)

(6) At the end of a shallow tank, we have $x = 0$, and the depth of water h is $h = h_0 x^{2m}$. Also the breadth of the tank b is given by $b = b_0 x^n$. Show that tidal waves of frequency $p/2\pi$ are possible, for which

$$\zeta = A x^u J_q(r x^s) \cos pt,$$

where

$$s = 1-m, \quad a^2 = p^2/gh_0, \quad r = a/s, \quad 2u = 1-2m-n \text{ and } q = |u/s|.$$

Use the fact that $J_m(x)$ satisfies the equation

$$\frac{d^2 J}{dx^2} + \frac{1}{x}\frac{dJ}{dx} + \left(1 - \frac{m^2}{x^2}\right) J = 0.$$

(7) Prove directly from the conditions (i)-(v) in § 47 without using the results of § 48 that the velocity of surface waves in a rectangular channel of infinite depth is $\sqrt{(g\lambda/2\pi)}$.

(8) Find the paths of particles of fluid in the case of surface waves on an infinitely deep circular tank of radius a.

(9) A tank of depth h is in the form of a sector of a circle of radius a and angle $72°$. What are the allowed normal modes for surface waves ?

(10) If X, Y, Z denotes the displacement of a particle of fluid from its mean position x, y, z in a rectangular tank of sides a and b when surface waves given by equation (37) are occurring, prove that the path of the particle is the straight line

$$\frac{a}{p\pi}\cot\frac{p\pi x}{a} X = \frac{b}{q\pi}\cot\frac{q\pi y}{b} Y = \frac{1}{r}\coth r(z+h) Z.$$

(11) Show that in surface waves on a cylindrical tank of radius a and depth h, the energies given by the normal modes (39) are

$$V = \frac{2\pi^3 D^2 f^2 \rho}{g} \cosh^2 nh \, \cos^2 2\pi ft \int_0^a J_m^2(nr) \, r \, dr, \text{ and}$$

$$T = \frac{1}{2} n\pi\rho D^2 \sin^2 2\pi ft \cosh nh \sinh nh \int_0^a J_m^2(nr) \, r \, dr.$$

Use the fact that the total energy must be independent of the time to deduce from this that the period equation is

$$4\pi^2 f^2 = gn \tanh nh.$$

(12) Show that when we use cylindrical polar coordinates to describe the capillary waves of § 53, the pressure condition at the free surface § 53 (iii) is

$$\frac{\partial \phi}{\partial t} - g\zeta + \frac{\mathsf{T}}{\rho} \left\{ \frac{\partial^2 \zeta}{\partial r^2} + \frac{1}{r} \frac{\partial \zeta}{\partial r} + \frac{1}{r^2} \frac{\partial^2 \zeta}{\partial \theta^2} \right\} = 0.$$

Use this result to show that waves of this nature on a circular basin of infinite depth are described by

$$\phi = C\, J_m(nr) \cos m\theta\, e^{nz} \cos 2\pi f t,$$

$$\zeta = \frac{-nC}{2\pi f}\, J_m(nr) \cos m\theta \sin 2\pi f t,$$

where $\quad J_m{'}(na) = 0$ and $4\pi^2 f^2 = gn + \mathsf{T}n^3/\rho.$

(13) Show that capillary waves on a rectangular basin of sides a, b and depth h are given by

$$\phi = A\, \frac{\cosh r(z+h)}{\sinh rh} \cos \frac{m\pi x}{a} \cos \frac{n\pi y}{b} \cos 2\pi f t,$$

$$\zeta = -\frac{rA}{2\pi f} \cos \frac{m\pi x}{a} \cos \frac{n\pi y}{b} \sin 2\pi f t,$$

where $m = 0, 1, 2, \ldots$; $n = 0, 1, 2 \ldots$; $r^2 = \pi^2(m^2/a^2 + n^2/b^2)$, and the period equation is

$$4\pi^2 f^2 = (gr + \mathsf{T}r^3/\rho) \tanh rh.$$

Verify, that when $n = 0$, this is equivalent to the result of § 54, equation (53).

[ANSWERS:

(1) $\frac{1}{4}\, g\rho la_r{}^2 \cos^2 \left(\frac{r\pi ct}{l} + \epsilon_r \right)$, $\frac{1}{4}\, g\rho la_r{}^2 \sin^2 \left(\frac{r\pi ct}{l} + \epsilon_r \right)$;

(2) radial vel. is $-(gA/c) \cos m\theta\, J_m{'}(nr) \sin(cnt + \epsilon)$, transverse velocity is $(gAm/cnr) \sin m\theta\, J_m(nr) \sin(cnt + \epsilon)$, $(gA/c)\, J_0{'}(nr)$; (3) $\zeta = A \cos(p\pi x/a) \cos(q\pi y/a) \cos(r\pi ct/a)$, $r^2 = p^2 + q^2$; K.E. $= \frac{1}{8}\, g\rho A^2 a^2 \sin^2(r\pi ct/a)$, P.E. $= \frac{1}{8}\, g\rho A^2 a^2 \cos^2(r\pi ct/a)$; (4) $\dfrac{X}{Y} = \dfrac{p}{q} \tan \dfrac{p\pi x}{a} \cot \dfrac{q\pi y}{a}$; (8) $X : Y : Z = nr J_m{'}(nr) : -m J_m(nr) \tan m\theta : nr\, J_m(nr)$; (9) Same as in eqns. (39)-(41) except that $m = 5k/2$, where $k = 0, 1, 2 \ldots$.]

CHAPTER VI

SOUND WAVES

§ 56. Throughout Chapter V we assumed that the liquid was incompressible. An important class of problems is that of waves in a compressible fluid, such as a gas. In this chapter we shall discuss such waves, of which sound waves are particular examples. The passage of a sound wave through a gas is accompanied by oscillatory motion of particles of the gas in the direction of wave propagation. These waves are therefore longitudinal. Since the density ρ is not constant, but varies with the pressure p, we require to know the relation between p and ρ. If the compressions and rarefactions that compose the wave succeed each other so slowly that the temperature remains constant (an *isothermal* change) this relation is $p = k\rho$. But normally this is not the case and no flow of heat, which would be needed to preserve the temperature constant, is possible ; in such cases (*adiabatic* changes)

$$p = k\rho^{\gamma}, \qquad . \qquad . \qquad . \qquad . \qquad (1)$$

where k and γ are constants depending on the particular gas used. We shall use (1) when it is required, rather than the isothermal relation

§ 57. There are several problems in the propagation of sound waves that can be solved without using the apparatus of velocity potential ϕ in the form in which we used it in Chapter V, §§ 47-54 ; we shall therefore discuss some of these before giving the general development of the subject.

Our first problem is that of waves along a uniform straight tube, or pipe, and we shall be able to solve this problem in a manner closely akin to that of Chapter IV, § **32**, where we discussed the longitudinal vibrations of a rod. We can suppose that the motion of the gas particles is entirely in the direction of the tube, and that the velocity and displacement are the same for all points of the same cross-section.

Suppose for convenience that the tube is of unit cross-sectional area, and let us consider the motion of that part of the gas originally confined between parallel planes at P and Q a distance dx apart (fig. 18). The plane P

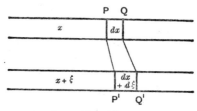

FIG. 18

is distant x from some fixed origin in the tube. During the vibration let PQ move to $P'Q'$, in which P is displaced a distance ξ from its mean position, and Q a distance $\xi + d\xi$. The length $P'Q'$ is therefore $dx + d\xi$. We shall find the equation of motion of the gas at $P'Q'$. For this purpose we shall require to know its mass and the pressure at its two ends. Its mass is the same as the mass of the undisturbed element PQ, viz. $\rho_0 dx$, where ρ_0 is the normal average density. To get the pressure at P' we imagine the element dx to shrink to zero; this gives the local density ρ, from which, by (1), we calculate the pressure. We have

$$\rho = \operatorname*{Lim}_{dx \to 0} \rho_0 dx / (dx + d\xi) = \rho_0 \left(1 - \frac{\partial \xi}{\partial x}\right), \qquad . \qquad (2)$$

if we may neglect powers of $\partial\xi/\partial x$ higher than the first. The quantity $(\rho-\rho_0)/\rho_0$ will often occur in this chapter; it is called the **condensation** s. Thus

$$s = -\partial\xi/\partial x, \quad \rho = \rho_0(1+s). \quad . \quad . \quad (3)$$

The net force acting on the element $P'Q'$ is $p_{P'}-p_{Q'}$, and hence the equation of motion is

$$\rho_0 dx \frac{\partial^2\xi}{\partial t^2} = p_{P'} - p_{Q'} = -\frac{\partial p}{\partial x}dx,$$

i.e.
$$\rho_0 \frac{\partial^2\xi}{\partial t^2} = -\frac{\partial p}{\partial x} \quad . \quad . \quad . \quad (4)$$

We may rewrite (4) in the form

$$\rho_0 \frac{\partial^2\xi}{\partial t^2} = -\frac{dp}{d\rho}\frac{\partial\rho}{\partial x} = \rho_0\frac{dp}{d\rho}\frac{\partial^2\xi}{\partial x^2} \qquad \text{from (2)}.$$

It appears then that ξ satisfies the familiar equation of wave motion

$$\frac{\partial^2\xi}{\partial x^2} = \frac{1}{c^2}\frac{\partial^2\xi}{\partial t^2}, \quad c^2 = dp/d\rho \quad . \quad . \quad (5)$$

This equation shows that waves of any shape will be transmitted in either direction with velocity $\sqrt{(dp/d\rho)}$. In the case of ordinary air at $0°$ C., using (1) as the relation between p and ρ, we find that the velocity is $c = 332$ metres per sec., which agrees with experiment. Newton, who made this calculation originally, took the isothermal relation between p and ρ and, naturally, obtained an incorrect value for the velocity of sound.

A more accurate calculation of the equation of motion can be made, in which powers of $\partial\xi/\partial x$ are not neglected, as follows. From (2) we have the accurate result

$$p = k\rho^\gamma = k\rho_0^\gamma \left/ \left(1+\frac{\partial\xi}{\partial x}\right)^\gamma\right.$$

So, now using (4) in which no approximations have been made,

$$\rho_0 \frac{\partial^2 \xi}{\partial t^2} = \frac{\gamma k \rho_0{}^\gamma}{\left(1+\dfrac{\partial \xi}{\partial x}\right)^{\gamma+1}} \frac{\partial^2 \xi}{\partial x^2},$$

i.e.
$$\frac{\partial^2 \xi}{\partial t^2} = \frac{\gamma p_0}{\rho_0} \frac{1}{\{1+\partial \xi/\partial x\}^{\gamma+1}} \frac{\partial^2 \xi}{\partial x^2} \qquad . \quad . \quad (6)$$

Equation (5) is found from (6) by neglecting $\partial \xi/\partial x$ compared with unity. A complete solution of (6) is, however, beyond the scope of this book. It is easy to see that, since (6) is not in the standard form of a wave equation, the velocity of transmission depends upon the frequency, and hence that a wave is not, in general, transmitted without change of shape.

§ 58. We must now discuss the boundary conditions. With an infinite tube, of course, there are no such conditions, but with a tube rigidly closed at $x = x_0$, we must have $\xi = 0$ at $x = x_0$, since at a fixed boundary the gas particles cannot move.

Another common type of boundary condition occurs when a tube has one or more ends open to the atmosphere. If we suppose that the waves inside the tube do not extend their influence to the air beyond the end of the tube, then at all open ends the pressure must have the normal atmospheric value, and thus, from (1) and (2), $\partial \xi/\partial x = 0$. Since the waves do extend a little outside the tube, this last equation is not strictly accurate. The usual modification is to increase the effective length of the tube by a small end-correction depending on the area of the cross-section of the tube. We shall not, however, include such corrections in this book.

To summarise :

(i) $\dfrac{\partial^2 \xi}{\partial x^2} = \dfrac{1}{c^2} \dfrac{\partial^2 \xi}{\partial t^2}$ in the tube, and $c^2 = dp/d\rho$. (5)

(ii) $\xi = 0$ at a closed end. . . . . (7)

(iii) $-\dfrac{\partial \xi}{\partial x} = s = 0$ at an open end. . . . (8)

§ **59**. We shall apply these equations to find the normal modes of vibration of gas in a tube of length l. These waves will naturally be of stationary type.

(a) *Closed at both ends* $x = 0$, l.—This problem is the same mathematically, as the transverse vibrations of a string of length l, fixed at its ends (cf. Chapter II, § **19**). Conditions (i) and (ii) of § **58** give for the normal modes

$$\xi = A_r \sin \frac{r\pi x}{l} \cos \left\{ \frac{r\pi ct}{l} + \epsilon_r \right\}, \ r = 1, 2, \dots. \quad (9)$$

(b) *Closed at* $x = 0$, *open at* $x = l$ (a " stopped tube ").— Here conditions (ii) and (iii) give $\xi = 0$ at $x = 0$, and $\dfrac{\partial \xi}{\partial x} = 0$ at $x = l$. The normal modes are

$$\xi = A_r \sin \left(r + \frac{1}{2} \right) \frac{\pi x}{l} \cos \left\{ \left(r + \frac{1}{2} \right) \frac{\pi ct}{l} + \epsilon_r \right\}, \ r = 0, 1, 2, \dots \quad (10)$$

(c) *Open at both ends* $x = 0$, l.—We have to satisfy the boundary condition (iii) $\partial \xi / \partial x = 0$ at $x = 0$, l. So the normal modes are

$$\xi = A_r \cos \frac{r\pi x}{l} \cos \left\{ \frac{r\pi ct}{l} + \epsilon_r \right\}, \ r = 1, 2, \dots \quad (11)$$

In each case the full solution would be the superposition of any number of terms of the appropriate type with different r. The fundamental periods in the three cases are $2l/c$, $4l/c$, and $2l/c$ respectively. The harmonics bear a simple numerical relationship to the fundamental, which explains the pleasant sound of an organ pipe.

§ **60**. We shall now solve a more complicated problem. We are to find the normal modes of a tube of unit sectional area, closed at one end by a rigid boundary and at the other by a mass M free to move along the tube. Let

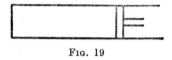

FIG. 19

the fixed boundary be taken as $x = 0$, and the normal equilibrium position of the moveable mass be at $x = l$ (fig. 19). Then we have to solve the standard equation of wave motion with the boundary conditions that when $x = 0$, (ii) gives $\xi = 0$, and that when $x = l$ the excess pressure inside, $p - p_0$, must be responsible for the acceleration of the mass M. This implies that

$$p - p_0 = M \frac{\partial^2 \xi}{\partial t^2} \text{ when } x = l.$$

The first condition is satisfied by the function

$$\xi = A \sin nx \cos (nct + \epsilon) . \qquad . \qquad . \qquad (12)$$

To satisfy the second condition, we observe that

$$p - p_0 = (dp/d\rho)(\rho - \rho_0) = -c^2 \rho_0 \partial \xi / \partial x, \text{ from } (3).$$

So this condition becomes

$$M \frac{\partial^2 \xi}{\partial t^2} = -c^2 \rho_0 \frac{\partial \xi}{\partial x} \quad \text{at } x = l.$$

Using (12) this gives, after a little reduction,

$$nl \tan nl = l \rho_0 / M.$$

The allowed values of n are the roots of this equation. There is an infinite number of them, and when $M = 0$, so that the tube is effectively open to the air at one end, we obtain equation (10) ; when $M = \infty$, so that the tube is closed at each end, we obtain equation (9).

§ 61. So far we have developed our solutions in terms

of ξ, the displacement of any particle of the gas from its mean position. It is possible, however, to use the method of the velocity potential ϕ. Many of the conditions which ϕ must satisfy are the same as in Chapter V, but a few of them are changed to allow for the variation in density. It is convenient to gather these various formulæ together first.

(i) If the motion is irrotational, as we shall assume,

$$\mathbf{u} = -\nabla\phi, \text{ (cf. Chapter V, equation (1)) } \quad . \quad (13)$$

(ii) At any fixed boundary, $\partial\phi/\partial\nu = 0$ (cf. Chapter V, equation (2)) . . . . (14)

(iii) The equation of Continuity (cf. Chapter V, equation (3)) is slightly altered, and it is *

$$\frac{\partial\rho}{\partial t} + \nabla\cdot\rho\mathbf{u} = 0,$$

i.e. $\quad \dfrac{\partial\rho}{\partial t} + \dfrac{\partial}{\partial x}(\rho u) + \dfrac{\partial}{\partial y}(\rho v) + \dfrac{\partial}{\partial z}(\rho w) = 0 \quad . \quad (15)$

(iv) The equations of motion are unchanged; if $\mathbf{F}$ is the external force on unit mass, in vector form, they are

$$\frac{D\mathbf{u}}{Dt} = \mathbf{F} - \frac{1}{\rho}\nabla p \quad \text{(cf. Chapter V, equation (6))} . \quad (16)$$

(v) In cases where the external forces have a potential V, we obtain Bernoulli's equation (cf. Chapter V, equation (8))

$$\int\frac{dp}{\rho} + \tfrac{1}{2}\mathbf{u}^2 + V - \frac{\partial\phi}{\partial t} = \text{const.} \quad . \quad . \quad (17)$$

in which we have absorbed an arbitrary function of the time into the term $\partial\phi/\partial t$ (cf. Chapter V, equation (8)).

§ 62. In sound waves we may neglect all external forces except such as occurs at boundaries, and thus we

* Rutherford, § 67.

may put $V = 0$ in (17). Also we may suppose that the velocities are small and neglect $\mathbf{u}^2$ in this equation. With these approximations Bernoulli's equation becomes

$$\int \frac{dp}{\rho} - \frac{\partial \phi}{\partial t} = \text{const.}$$

We can simplify the first term; for $\int \dfrac{dp}{\rho} = \int \left(\dfrac{dp}{d\rho}\right)\dfrac{d\rho}{\rho}$, and if the variations in density are small, $dp/d\rho$ may be taken as constant, and equal to c^2 as in (5). Thus

$$\int \frac{dp}{\rho} = c^2 \int \frac{d\rho}{\rho} = c^2 \log_e\rho = c^2\{\log_e(1+s)+\log_e\rho_0\}.$$

So $\int \dfrac{dp}{\rho} = c^2s+\text{const.}$, if s is small. If we absorb this constant in ϕ, then Bernoulli's equation takes its final form

$$c^2s-\partial\phi/\partial t = 0 \qquad . \qquad . \qquad . \qquad (18)$$

Laplace's equation for ϕ does not hold because of the changed equation of continuity. But if u, v, w and s are small, (15) can be written in a simpler form by the aid of (13); viz.,

$$\rho_0\partial s/\partial t-\rho\nabla^2\phi = 0.$$

This is effectively the same as

$$\frac{\partial s}{\partial t} = \nabla^2\phi \qquad \bullet \qquad \bullet \qquad \bullet \qquad (19)$$

Now let us eliminate s between (18) and (19), and we shall find the standard equation of wave motion

$$\nabla^2\phi = \frac{1}{c^2}\frac{\partial^2\phi}{\partial t^2} \qquad \bullet \qquad \bullet \qquad \bullet \qquad (20)$$

This shows that c is indeed the velocity of wave propagation, but before we can use this technique for solving problems, we must first obtain the boundary conditions for ϕ. At a fixed boundary, by (ii) $\partial\phi/\partial\nu = 0$. At an open end of a tube, the pressure must be atmospheric, and hence $s = 0$. Thus, from (18),

$$\partial\phi/\partial t = 0. \qquad . \qquad . \qquad . \qquad . \qquad (21)$$

This completes the development of the method of the velocity potential, and we can choose in any particular problem whether we solve by means of the displacement ξ or the potential ϕ. It is possible to pass from one to the other, since from (3) and (18)

$$\frac{\partial\xi}{\partial x} = -s = -\frac{1}{c^2}\frac{\partial\phi}{\partial t}. \qquad . \qquad . \qquad (22)$$

§ 63. We shall illustrate these equations by solving the problem of stationary waves in a tube of length l, closed at one end ($x = 0$) and open at the other ($x = l$). This is the problem already dealt with in § 59 (b), and with the same notation, we require a solution of $\dfrac{\partial^2\phi}{\partial x^2} = \dfrac{1}{c^2}\dfrac{\partial^2\phi}{\partial t^2}$ subject to the conditions

$$\partial\phi/\partial x = 0 \text{ at } x = 0,$$
$$\partial\phi/\partial t = 0 \text{ at } x = l.$$

It is easily seen that

$$\phi = a \cos mx \cos (cmt + \epsilon)$$

satisfies all these conditions provided that $\cos ml = 0$, i.e. $ml = \pi/2,\ 3\pi/2,\ \ldots\ (r+\tfrac{1}{2})\pi\ \ldots$. So the normal modes are

$$\phi = a_r \cos\left(r+\frac{1}{2}\right)\frac{\pi x}{l}\cos\left\{\left(r+\frac{1}{2}\right)\frac{\pi ct}{l} + \epsilon_r\right\},$$

and from this expression all the other properties of these waves may easily be obtained. The student is advised to treat the problems of § 59 (a) and (c) in a similar manner.

§ 64. Our next application of the equations of § 62 will be to problems where there is spherical symmetry about the origin. The fundamental equation of wave motion then becomes (see Chapter I, equation (23))

$$\frac{\partial^2\phi}{\partial r^2} + \frac{2}{r}\frac{\partial\phi}{\partial r} = \frac{1}{c^2}\frac{\partial^2\phi}{\partial t^2},$$

with solutions of progressive type

$$\phi = \frac{1}{r}f(r-ct) + \frac{1}{r}g(r+ct).$$

There are solutions of stationary type (see Chapter I, equation (37))

$$\phi = r^{-1} \frac{\cos}{\sin} mr \frac{\cos}{\sin} cmt.$$

If the gas is contained inside a fixed sphere of radius a then we must have ϕ finite when $r = 0$, and $\partial\phi/\partial r = 0$ when $r = a$. This means that

$$\phi = \frac{A}{r} \sin mr \cos(cmt+\epsilon),$$

with the condition

$$\tan ma = ma \quad . \quad . \quad . \quad . \quad (23)$$

This period equation has an infinite number of roots which approximate to $ma = (n+1/2)\pi$ when n is large. So for its higher frequencies the system behaves very like a uniform pipe of length a open at one end and closed at the other.

This analysis would evidently equally well apply to describe waves in a conical pipe.

§ 65. We shall now calculate the energy in a sound wave. The Kinetic energy is clearly $\int \frac{1}{2}\rho\mathbf{u}^2 dV$, where dV is an element of volume. We may put $\rho = \rho_0$ without loss of accuracy. In terms of the velocity potential this may be written

$$\int \frac{1}{2}\rho_0(\nabla\phi)^2 dV = -\frac{1}{2}\rho_0 \int \phi\nabla^2\phi dV + \frac{1}{2}\rho_0 \int \phi\frac{\partial\phi}{\partial\nu}dS \quad . \quad (24)$$

The last expression follows from Green's theorem just as in Chapter V, § 51, and the surface integral is taken over the boundary of the gas. There is also Potential energy because each small volume of gas is compressed or rarified, and work is stored up in the process. To calculate it, consider a small volume V_0, which during the passage of a wave is changed to V_1. If s_1 is the corresponding value of the condensation, then from (3), we have, to the first degree in s_1,

$$V_1 = V_0(1-s_1) \qquad . \qquad . \qquad . \qquad (25)$$

Further, suppose that during the process of compression, V and s are simultaneous intermediary values. Then we can write the work done in compressing the volume from V_0 to V_1 in the form $-\int_{V_0}^{V_1} p \, dV$. But, just as in (25), $V = V_0(1-s)$, and hence

$$dV = -V_0 \, ds.$$

We may also write $p = p_0 + (dp/d\rho)(\rho - \rho_0)$
$$= p_0 + c^2\rho_0 s.$$

Thus the potential energy may be written

$$\int_0^{s_1} (p_0 + c^2\rho_0 s) V_0 ds = p_0 V_0 s_1 + \tfrac{1}{2}c^2\rho_0 V_0 s_1{}^2$$
$$= p_0(V_0 - V_1) + \tfrac{1}{2}c^2\rho_0 V_0 s_1{}^2.$$

This is the contribution to the P.E. which arises from the volume V_0. The total P.E. may be found by integration. The first term will vanish in this process since it merely represents the total change in volume of the gas, which we may suppose to be zero. We conclude, therefore, that

the Potential Energy is $\int \dfrac{1}{2} c^2\rho_0 s^2 dV$ . . . . (26)

It can easily be shown that with a progressive wave the K.E. and P.E. are equal; this does not hold for stationary waves, for which their sum remains constant.

§ **66**. We conclude this chapter with a discussion of the propagation of waves along a pipe whose cross-sectional area A varies slowly along its length. Our discussion is similar in many respects to the analysis in § **57**.

Consider the pipe shown in fig. 20, and let us measure distances x along the central line. It will be approximately true to say that the velocity u is constant across any section perpendicular to the x axis. Suppose that the gas originally confined between the two places P, Q at

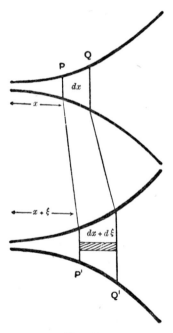

Fig. 20

distances x, $x+dx$ is displaced during the passage of a wave, to $P'Q'$, the displacement of P being ξ and of Q being $\xi+d\xi$. Consider the motion of a small prism of gas

such as that shaded in the figure ; its equation of motion
may be found as in § **57**, and it is

$$\rho_0 \frac{\partial^2 \xi}{\partial t^2} = - \frac{\partial p}{\partial x} \qquad . \qquad . \qquad . \quad (27)$$

We must therefore find the pressure in terms of ξ. This
may be obtained from the equation of continuity, which
expresses the fact that the mass of gas in $P'Q'$ is the same
as that in PQ. Thus, if ρ is the density,

$$\rho_0 A(x)\, dx = \rho\, A(x+\xi)\, . \{dx+d\xi\},$$

i.e. $$\rho_0 A(x) = \rho \left\{ A(x) + \xi \frac{\partial A}{\partial x} \right\} \left\{ 1 + \frac{\partial \xi}{\partial x} \right\}.$$

Neglecting small quantities, this yields

$$\rho_0 = \rho \left\{ 1 + \frac{\partial \xi}{\partial x} + \frac{\xi}{A} \frac{\partial A}{\partial x} \right\}.$$

Therefore

$$\rho = \rho_0 \left\{ 1 - \frac{\partial \xi}{\partial x} - \frac{\xi}{A} \frac{\partial A}{\partial x} \right\} = \rho_0 \left\{ 1 - \frac{1}{A} \frac{\partial}{\partial x} (A\xi) \right\}. \quad (28)$$

Eliminating p between (27) and (28) we find

$$\rho_0 \frac{\partial^2 \xi}{\partial t^2} = - \frac{dp}{d\rho} \frac{\partial \rho}{\partial x} = c^2 \rho_0 \frac{\partial}{\partial x} \left\{ \frac{1}{A} \frac{\partial}{\partial x} (A\xi) \right\},$$

where, as usual, $$c^2 = \frac{dp}{d\rho}.$$

So the equation of motion is

$$\frac{\partial^2 \xi}{\partial t^2} = c^2 \frac{\partial}{\partial x} \left\{ \frac{1}{A} \frac{\partial}{\partial x} (A\xi) \right\} \qquad . \qquad . \qquad . \quad (29)$$

In the case in which A is constant this reduces to the former
equation (5). An important example when A is not

constant is the so-called exponential horn used on the best acoustic gramophones ; here the tube is approximately symmetrical about its central line and the area varies with the distance according to the law $A = A_0 e^{2ax}$, where a and A_0 are constants.

With this form of A, (29) reduces to

$$\frac{\partial^2 \xi}{\partial t^2} = c^2 \left\{ \frac{\partial^2 \xi}{\partial x^2} + 2a \frac{\partial \xi}{\partial x} \right\}.$$

A solution is possible by the method of separation of variables (see § 7). We soon find

$$\xi = e^{icnt}\{B_1 e^{m_1 x} + B_2 e^{m_2 x}\},$$

where m_1 and m_2 are given by $-a \pm \sqrt{(a^2 - n^2)}$. In most exponential horns n^2 is considerably larger than a^2 in the range of audible frequencies, so that m_1 and m_2 may be written $-a \pm in$. Thus

$$\xi = e^{-ax}\{B_1 e^{in(ct-x)} + B_2 e^{in(ct+x)}\}. \qquad . \qquad (30)$$

The first term represents a wave going outwards and the second a wave coming inwards. We conclude from this that waves can be sent outwards along the horn with a velocity c which is approximately independent of the frequency, and with an attenuation factor e^{-ax} which is also independent of the frequency. It is this double independence which allows good reproduction of whatever waves are generated at the narrow end of the horn, and which is responsible for this choice of shape in the best gramophones. Other forms of A will not, in general, give rise to the same behaviour.

§ 67.   Examples

(1) Use the method of § 58 to investigate sound waves in a closed rectangular box of sides a_1, a_2 and a_3. Show that if the box is large, the number of such waves for which the frequency is less than n is approximately equal to one-eighth of the

volume of the quadric $x^2/a_1{}^2 + y^2/a_2{}^2 + z^2/a_3{}^2 = 4n^2/c^2$. Hence show that this number is approximately $4\pi n^3 a_1 a_2 a_3/3c^3$.

(2) Investigate the reflection and transmission of a train of harmonic waves in a uniform straight tube at a point where a smooth piston of mass M just fits into the tube and is free to move.

(3) Show that the kinetic and potential energies of a plane progressive wave are equal.

(4) Show that the kinetic and potential energies of stationary waves in a rectangular box have a constant sum.

(5) Find an equation for the normal modes of a gas which is confined between two rigid concentric spheres of radii a and b.

(6) Show that a closer approximation to the roots of equation (23) is $ma = (n+\tfrac{1}{2})\pi - 1/\{(n+\tfrac{1}{2})\pi\}$.

(7) Find numerically the fundamental frequency of a conical pipe of radius 1 metre open at its wide end.

(8) The cross-sectional area of a closed tube varies with the distance along its central line according to the law $A = A_0 x^n$. Show that if its two ends are $x = 0$, and $x = l$, then standing waves can exist in the tube for which the displacement is given by the formula

$$\xi = x^{(1-n)/2} J_m(qx/c) \cos \{qct + \epsilon\},$$

where $\quad m = (n+1)/2 \quad$ and $\quad J_m(ql/c) = 0$.

Use the fact that $J_m(x)$ satisfies the equation

$$\frac{d^2 J}{dx^2} + \frac{1}{x}\frac{dJ}{dx} + \left(1 - \frac{m^2}{x^2}\right) J = 0.$$

[ANSWERS: 2. reflection coefft. $R = \{1 + 4\rho_0{}^2/M^2 n^2\}^{-1}$, transmission coefft. $T = \{1 + M^2 n^2/4\rho_0{}^2\}^{-1}$; for definitions of R and T see § 16; 5. period $= 2\pi/pc$, where $(abp^2 + 1)\sin p(b-a) = p(b-a)\cos p(b-a)$; 7. 166 per sec.]

CHAPTER VII

ELECTRIC WAVES *

§ 68. Before we discuss the propagation of electric waves, we shall summarise the most important equations that we shall require. These are known as **Maxwell's equations.** Let the vectors **E** (components E_x, E_y, E_z) and **H** (components H_x, H_y, H_z) denote the **electric** and **magnetic field strengths**. These are defined † as the forces on a unit charge or pole respectively when placed inside a small needle-shaped cavity, the direction of the cavity being the same as the direction in which we wish to measure the component of **E** or **H**. We shall suppose that all our media are isotropic with no ferromagnetism or permanent polarisation ; thus, if we write ϵ for the dielectric constant, and μ for the permeability, then the related vectors, viz. the **magnetic induction B** and the **dielectric displacement D** are given by the equations $\mathbf{B} = \mu\mathbf{H}$, $\mathbf{D} = \epsilon\mathbf{E}$. Further, let **j** (components j_x, j_y, j_z) denote the current density vector, and ρ the charge density. Then, if we measure **j**, **B** and **H** in electromagnetic units, **E** and **D** in electrostatic units, writing c for the ratio between the two sets of units,‡ Maxwell's equations may be summarised in vector form as follows :

$$\operatorname{div} \mathbf{D} = 4\pi\rho \qquad \cdot \qquad \cdot \qquad \cdot \qquad \cdot \qquad \cdot \qquad (1)$$

$$\operatorname{div} \mathbf{B} = 0 \ . \qquad \cdot \qquad \cdot \qquad \cdot \qquad \cdot \qquad (2)$$

* Before reading this chapter, the student is advised to familiarise himself with the equations of electromagnetism, as found in text books such as those by Jeans, Pidduck, Abraham-Becker or the present writer.

† See, e.g., Coulson, *Electricity*, Oliver and Boyd, Chapter II, VI.

‡ This system is known as the Mixed System. If we had used entirely e.s.u., or entirely e.m.u., the powers of c would have been different. Particular care is required in discussing the units in (3) and (7). In this chapter c will always denote the ratio of the two sets of units.

Date	Time	Clinic	Physician/Surgeon

Comments and suggestions concerning the Hospital should be sent to the Hospital Secretary.

QUEEN MARY'S HOSPITAL
Roehampton

Telephone: 01-789 6611

Name: Dr. G REEN, M

No. S 8763

When appointment cannot be kept, please notify Appointments Clerk.

Date	Time	Clinic	Physician/Surgeon	
4.2.77	10.30	Mr O. WAMS		
11.11.77	10 c			
10.3.81	9.30	Dur	m Dunphlay	

THIS CARD MUST BE BROUGHT ON EACH ATTENDANCE. PLEASE REPORT TO RECEPTION ON ARRIVAL.

C2.

$$\text{curl } \mathbf{H} = 4\pi\mathbf{j} + \frac{1}{c}\frac{\partial \mathbf{D}}{\partial t} \quad . \quad . \quad . \quad . \quad (3)$$

$$\text{curl } \mathbf{E} = -\frac{1}{c}\frac{\partial \mathbf{B}}{\partial t} \quad . \quad . \quad . \quad . \quad (4)$$

$$\mathbf{D} = \epsilon\mathbf{E} \quad . \quad . \quad . \quad . \quad . \quad (5)$$

$$\mathbf{B} = \mu\mathbf{H}. \quad . \quad . \quad . \quad . \quad (6)$$

To these equations we must add the relation between $\mathbf{j}$ and $\mathbf{E}$. If σ is the **conductivity**, which is the inverse of the **specific resistance**, this relation is

$$\mathbf{j} = \sigma\mathbf{E} \quad . \quad . \quad . \quad . \quad (7)$$

For conductors σ is large, and for insulators it is small.

The above equations have been written in vector form; until the student has acquired familiarity with the use of the vector notation and operation, he is advised to verify the various calculations of this chapter, using the equations in Cartesian form as well as vector form. This will soon show how much simpler the vector treatment is, in nearly every case. If we wish to write these equations in their full Cartesian form, we have to remember that

$$\text{div } \mathbf{D} \equiv \nabla \cdot \mathbf{D} = \frac{\partial D_x}{\partial x} + \frac{\partial D_y}{\partial y} + \frac{\partial D_z}{\partial z} \text{ and that}$$

$$\text{curl } \mathbf{H} \equiv \nabla \times \mathbf{H} = \left(\frac{\partial H_z}{\partial y} - \frac{\partial H_y}{\partial z}, \frac{\partial H_x}{\partial z} - \frac{\partial H_z}{\partial x}, \frac{\partial H_y}{\partial x} - \frac{\partial H_x}{\partial y}\right).$$

The preceding equations then become

$$\frac{\partial D_x}{\partial x} + \frac{\partial D_y}{\partial y} + \frac{\partial D_z}{\partial z} = 4\pi\rho \quad (1') \qquad \frac{\partial B_x}{\partial x} + \frac{\partial B_y}{\partial y} + \frac{\partial B_z}{\partial z} = 0 \quad (2')$$

$$\left.\begin{aligned}
\frac{\partial H_z}{\partial y} - \frac{\partial H_y}{\partial z} &= 4\pi j_x + \frac{1}{c}\frac{\partial D_x}{\partial t}\\[1ex]
\frac{\partial H_x}{\partial z} - \frac{\partial H_z}{\partial x} &= 4\pi j_y + \frac{1}{c}\frac{\partial D_y}{\partial t}\\[1ex]
\frac{\partial H_y}{\partial x} - \frac{\partial H_x}{\partial y} &= 4\pi j_z + \frac{1}{c}\frac{\partial D_z}{\partial t}
\end{aligned}\right\} (3') \qquad
\left.\begin{aligned}
\frac{\partial E_z}{\partial y} - \frac{\partial E_y}{\partial z} &= -\frac{1}{c}\frac{\partial B_x}{\partial t}\\[1ex]
\frac{\partial E_x}{\partial z} - \frac{\partial E_z}{\partial x} &= -\frac{1}{c}\frac{\partial B_y}{\partial t}\\[1ex]
\frac{\partial E_y}{\partial x} - \frac{\partial E_x}{\partial y} &= -\frac{1}{c}\frac{\partial B_z}{\partial t}
\end{aligned}\right\} (4')$$

$$D_x = \epsilon E_x \ , \ D_y = \epsilon E_y \ , \ D_z = \epsilon E_z \quad . \quad . \quad (5')$$
$$B_x = \mu H_x \ , \ B_y = \mu H_y \ , \ B_z = \mu H_z \quad . \quad . \quad (6')$$
$$j_x = \sigma E_x \ , \ j_y = \sigma E_y \ , \ j_z = \sigma E_z \quad . \quad . \quad (7')$$

Equations (1)-(4) are sometimes called Maxwell's Equations and equations (5)-(7) **constitutive relations**. Simple physical bases can easily be given for (1)-(4). Thus, (1) represents Gauss' Theorem, and follows from the law of force between two charges ; (2) represents the fact that isolated magnetic poles cannot be obtained ; (3) is Ampère's Rule that the work done in carrying a unit pole round a closed circuit equals 4π times the total current enclosed in the circuit ; part of this current is the conduction current $\mathbf{j}$ and part is Maxwell's displacement current $\dfrac{1}{4\pi c} \dfrac{\partial \mathbf{D}}{\partial t}$; (4) is Lenz's law of induction.

These seven equations represent the basis of our subsequent work. They need to be supplemented by a statement of the boundary conditions that hold at a change of medium. If suffix n denotes the component normal to the boundary of the two media, and suffix s denotes the component in any direction in the boundary plane, then on passing from the one medium to the other

$$D_n, \ B_n, \ E_s \text{ and } H_s \text{ are continuous} \quad . \quad . \quad (8)$$

In cases where there is a current sheet (i.e. a finite current flowing in an indefinitely thin surface layer) some of these conditions need modification, but we shall not discuss any such cases in this chapter.

There are two other important results that we shall use. First, we may suppose that the electromagnetic field stores energy, and the density of this energy per unit volume of the medium is

$$\frac{1}{8\pi} \{ \epsilon \mathbf{E}^2 + \mu \mathbf{H}^2 \} \quad . \quad . \quad . \quad (9)$$

Second, there is a vector, known as the **Poynting**

vector, which is concerned with the rate at which energy is flowing. This vector, whose magnitude and direction are given by

$$\frac{c}{4\pi} (\mathbf{E} \times \mathbf{H}), \qquad . \qquad . \qquad . \qquad . \qquad (10)$$

represents the amount of energy which flows in unit time across unit area drawn perpendicular to it. $\mathbf{E}$ and $\mathbf{H}$ are generally rapidly varying quantities and in such cases it is the mean value of (10) that has physical significance.

§ **69.** We shall first deal with non-conducting media, such as glass, so that we may put $\sigma = 0$ in (7); we suppose that the medium is homogeneous, i.e. ϵ and μ are constants. If, as usually happens, there is no residual charge, we may also put $\rho = 0$ in (1), and with these simplifications, Maxwell's equations may be written

$$\left.\begin{array}{l} \operatorname{div} \mathbf{E} = 0 \ , \ \operatorname{div} \mathbf{H} = 0, \\[2mm] \operatorname{curl} \mathbf{E} = -\ \dfrac{\mu}{c} \dfrac{\partial \mathbf{H}}{\partial t}, \ \ \operatorname{curl} \mathbf{H} = \dfrac{\epsilon}{c} \dfrac{\partial \mathbf{E}}{\partial t} \end{array}\right\} \quad . \quad (11)$$

These equations lead immediately to the standard equation of wave motion, for we know * that

$$\operatorname{curl} \operatorname{curl} \mathbf{H} = \operatorname{grad} \operatorname{div} \mathbf{H} - \nabla^2 \mathbf{H}.$$

Consequently, from the fourth of the equations in (11), we find

$$\operatorname{grad} \operatorname{div} \mathbf{H} - \nabla^2 \mathbf{H} = \frac{\epsilon}{c} \operatorname{curl} \frac{\partial \mathbf{E}}{\partial t} = \frac{\epsilon}{c} \frac{\partial}{\partial t} \operatorname{curl} \mathbf{E}.$$

Substituting for div $\mathbf{H}$ and curl $\mathbf{E}$, we discover the standard equation

$$\nabla^2 \mathbf{H} = \frac{\epsilon \mu}{c^2} \frac{\partial^2 \mathbf{H}}{\partial t^2} \qquad . \qquad . \qquad . \qquad (12)$$

* Rutherford, *Vector Methods*, p. 59, equation (10).

Eliminating **H** instead of **E** we find the same equation for **E**.

$$\nabla^2 \mathbf{E} = \frac{\epsilon\mu}{c^2}\frac{\partial^2 \mathbf{E}}{\partial t^2} \qquad \cdot \qquad \cdot \qquad \cdot \qquad (13)$$

According to our discussion of this equation in Chapter I, this shows that waves can be propagated in such a medium, and that their velocity is $c/\sqrt{(\epsilon\mu)}$. In free space, where $\epsilon = \mu = 1$, this velocity is just c. Now c, which was defined as the ratio of the two sets of electrical units, has the dimensions of a velocity, and its magnitude can be obtained experimentally; it is approximately $2 \cdot 998 . 10^{10}$ cms. per sec. But it is known that the velocity of light in free space has exactly this same value. We are thus led to the conviction that light waves are electromagnetic in nature, a view that has subsequently received complete verification. X-rays, γ-rays, ultra-violet waves, infra-red waves and wireless waves are also electromagnetic, and differ only in the order of magnitude of their wavelengths. We shall be able to show later, in § **71**, that these waves are transverse.

In non-conducting dielectric media, like glass, ϵ is not equal to unity ; also μ depends on the frequency of the waves, but for light waves in the visible region we may put $\mu = 1$. The velocity of light is therefore $c/\sqrt{\epsilon}$. Now in a medium whose refractive index is K, it is known experimentally that the velocity of light is c/K. Hence, if our original assumptions are valid, $\epsilon = K^2$. This is known as **Maxwell's relation**. It holds good for many substances, but fails because it does not take sufficiently detailed account of the atomic structure of the dielectric. It applies better for long waves (low frequency) than for short waves (high frequency).

§ **70.** A somewhat different discussion of (11) can be given in terms of the electric and magnetic potentials. Since div **B** = 0, it follows that we can write

$$\mathbf{B} = \mu\mathbf{H} = \operatorname{curl} \mathbf{A}, \qquad \cdot \qquad \cdot \qquad \cdot \qquad (14)$$

where **A** is a vector yet to be determined. This equation does not define **A** completely, since if ψ is any scalar, curl $(\mathbf{A}+\text{grad } \psi) = \text{curl } \mathbf{A}$. Thus **A** is undefined to the extent of addition of the gradient of any scalar, and we may accordingly impose one further condition upon it.

If $\mathbf{B} = \text{curl } \mathbf{A}$, and curl $\mathbf{E} = -\dfrac{1}{c}\dfrac{\partial \mathbf{B}}{\partial t}$, it follows, by elimination of **B**, that

$$\text{curl} \left\{ \mathbf{E} + \frac{1}{c}\frac{\partial \mathbf{A}}{\partial t} \right\} = 0.$$

Integrating,

$$\mathbf{E} + \frac{1}{c}\frac{\partial \mathbf{A}}{\partial t} = -\text{grad } \phi,$$

where ϕ is an arbitrary scalar function,

i.e.
$$\mathbf{E} = -\text{grad } \phi - \frac{1}{c}\frac{\partial \mathbf{A}}{\partial t} \qquad \bullet \quad \bullet \quad (15)$$

In cases where there is no variation with the time, this becomes $\mathbf{E} = -\text{grad } \phi$, showing that ϕ is the analogue of the electrostatic potential.

Eliminating **H** from the relations $\mu\mathbf{H} = \text{curl } \mathbf{A}$, curl $\mathbf{H} = \dfrac{\epsilon}{c}\dfrac{\partial \mathbf{E}}{\partial t}$, and using (15) to eliminate **E**, we find

$$\text{grad div } \mathbf{A} - \nabla^2 \mathbf{A} = -\frac{\mu\epsilon}{c}\text{ grad }\frac{\partial \phi}{\partial t} - \frac{\epsilon\mu}{c^2}\frac{\partial^2 \mathbf{A}}{\partial t^2}.$$

i.e.
$$\nabla^2 \mathbf{A} = \frac{\epsilon\mu}{c^2}\frac{\partial^2 \mathbf{A}}{\partial t^2} + \text{grad}\left\{ \text{div } \mathbf{A} + \frac{\mu\epsilon}{c}\frac{\partial \phi}{\partial t} \right\}.$$

Let us now introduce the extra allowed condition upon **A**, and write

$$\text{div } \mathbf{A} + \frac{\mu\epsilon}{c}\frac{\partial \phi}{\partial t} = 0 \quad . \qquad . \qquad . \qquad (16)$$

Then **A** satisfies the standard equation of wave motion

$$\nabla^2 \mathbf{A} = \frac{\epsilon\mu}{c^2}\frac{\partial^2 \mathbf{A}}{\partial t^2} \qquad . \qquad . \qquad . \qquad (17)$$

Further, taking the divergence of (15), we obtain, by (16)

$$0 = \text{div } \mathbf{E} = -\nabla^2\phi - \frac{1}{c}\frac{\partial}{\partial t}\text{ div } \mathbf{A} = -\nabla^2\phi + \frac{\epsilon\mu}{c^2}\frac{\partial^2\phi}{\partial t^2}.$$

Thus ϕ also satisfies the standard equation

$$\nabla^2\phi = \frac{\epsilon\mu}{c^2}\frac{\partial^2\phi}{\partial t^2} \qquad \cdot \qquad \cdot \qquad \cdot \qquad \cdot \qquad (18)$$

A similar analysis can be carried through when ρ and $\mathbf{j}$ are not put equal to zero, and we find

$$\mathbf{B} = \text{curl } \mathbf{A} \qquad \cdot \qquad \cdot \qquad \cdot \qquad \cdot \qquad (14')$$

$$\mathbf{E} = -\text{grad } \phi - \frac{1}{c}\frac{\partial \mathbf{A}}{\partial t} \qquad \cdot \qquad \cdot \qquad (15')$$

$$0 = \text{div } \mathbf{A} + \frac{\mu\epsilon}{c}\frac{\partial \phi}{\partial t} \qquad \cdot \qquad \cdot \qquad (16')$$

$$\nabla^2\mathbf{A} = \frac{\epsilon\mu}{c^2}\frac{\partial^2\mathbf{A}}{\partial t^2} - 4\pi\mu\mathbf{j} \qquad \cdot \qquad \cdot \qquad (17')$$

$$\nabla^2\phi = \frac{\epsilon\mu}{c^2}\frac{\partial^2\phi}{\partial t^2} - \frac{4\pi\rho}{\epsilon} \qquad \cdot \qquad \cdot \qquad (18')$$

ϕ and **A** are known as the **electric potential** and **magnetic** or **vector potential** respectively. It is open to our choice whether we solve problems in terms of **A** and ϕ, or of **E** and **H**. The relations (14')-(18') enable us to pass from the one system to the other. The boundary conditions for ϕ and **A** may easily be obtained from (8), but since we shall always adopt the **E**, **H** type of solution, which is usually the simpler, there is no need to write them down here.

There is one other general deduction that can be made here. If we use (3), (5) and (7) we can write, for homogeneous media,

$$\text{curl } \mathbf{H} = 4\pi\sigma\mathbf{E} + \frac{\epsilon}{c}\frac{\partial \mathbf{E}}{\partial t}.$$

Taking the divergence of each side, and noting, from (1), that div $\mathbf{E} = 4\pi\rho/\epsilon$, we find

$$\frac{\epsilon}{c}\frac{\partial\rho}{\partial t} + 4\pi\sigma\rho = 0.$$

Thus, on integration,

$$\rho = \rho_0 e^{-t/\theta}, \text{ where } \theta = \epsilon/4\pi\sigma c \quad . \quad . \quad (19)$$

θ is called the **time of relaxation**. It follows from (19) that any original distribution of charge decays exponentially at a rate quite independent of any other electromagnetic disturbances that may be taking place simultaneously, and it justifies us in putting $\rho = 0$ in most of our problems. With metals such as copper, θ is of the order of 10^{-13} secs., and is beyond measurement; but with dielectrics such as water θ is large enough to be determined experimentally. Equation (19) only applies to the charge at an internal point in a medium; charges at the boundary of a conductor or insulator do not obey this equation at all.

§ **71.** We next discuss plane waves in a uniform non-conducting medium, and show that they are of transverse type, $\mathbf{E}$ and $\mathbf{H}$ being perpendicular to the direction of propagation. Let us consider plane waves travelling with velocity V in a direction l, m, n. Then $\mathbf{E}$ and $\mathbf{H}$ must be functions of a new variable

$$u \equiv lx + my + nz - Vt \quad . \quad . \quad . \quad (20)$$

When we say that a vector such as $\mathbf{E}$ is a function of u, we mean that each of its three components separately is a function of u, though the three functions need not be the same. Consider the fourth equation of (11). Its x-component (see (3')) is

$$\frac{\partial H_z}{\partial y} - \frac{\partial H_y}{\partial z} = \frac{\epsilon}{c}\frac{\partial E_x}{\partial t}.$$

If dashes denote differentiation with respect to u, this is

$$mH_z' - nH_y' = -\frac{\epsilon V}{c} E_x'.$$

Integrating with respect to u, this becomes

$$mH_z - nH_y = -\frac{\epsilon V}{c} E_x,$$

in which we have put the constant of integration equal to zero, since we are concerned with fluctuating fields whose mean value is zero. There are two similar equations to the above, for E_y and E_z, and we may write them as one vector equation. If we let $\mathbf{n}$ denote the unit vector in the direction of propagation, so that $\mathbf{n} = (l, m, n)$, we have

$$\mathbf{n} \times \mathbf{H} = -\frac{\epsilon V}{c} \mathbf{E} \quad . \quad . \quad . \quad . \quad (21)$$

Exactly similar treatment is possible for the third equation of (11); we get

$$\mathbf{n} \times \mathbf{E} = \frac{\mu V}{c} \mathbf{H} \quad . \quad . \quad . \quad . \quad (22)$$

Equation (21) shows that $\mathbf{E}$ is perpendicular to $\mathbf{n}$ and $\mathbf{H}$, and (22) shows that $\mathbf{H}$ is perpendicular to $\mathbf{n}$ and $\mathbf{E}$. In other words, both $\mathbf{E}$ and $\mathbf{H}$ are perpendicular to the direction of propagation, so that the waves are transverse, and in addition, $\mathbf{E}$ and $\mathbf{H}$ are themselves perpendicular, $\mathbf{E}$, $\mathbf{H}$ and $\mathbf{n}$ forming a right-handed set of axes. If we eliminate $\mathbf{H}$ from (21) and (22) and use the fact that

$$\mathbf{n} \times [\mathbf{n} \times \mathbf{E}] = (\mathbf{n} \cdot \mathbf{E})\mathbf{n} - (\mathbf{n} \cdot \mathbf{n})\mathbf{E} = -\mathbf{E},$$

since $\mathbf{n}$ is perpendicular to $\mathbf{E}$ and $\mathbf{n}$ is a unit vector, we discover that $V^2 = c^2/\epsilon\mu$, showing again that the velocity of these waves is indeed $c/\sqrt{(\epsilon\mu)}$.

It is worth while writing down the particular cases of (21) and (22) that correspond to plane harmonic waves in the direction of the z axis, and with the **E** vector in the x or y directions. The solutions are

$$
\begin{aligned}
E_x &= 0 & H_x &= -\sqrt{(\epsilon/\mu)}\, a e^{ip(t-z/V)} \\
E_y &= a e^{ip(t-z/V)} & H_y &= 0 \\
E_z &= 0 & H_z &= 0.
\end{aligned}
\tag{23}
$$

$$
\begin{aligned}
E_x &= b e^{ip(t-z/V)} & H_x &= 0 \\
E_y &= 0 & H_y &= +\sqrt{(\epsilon/\mu)}\, b e^{ip(t-z/V)} \\
E_z &= 0 & H_z &= 0.
\end{aligned}
\tag{24}
$$

In accordance with § **10**, a and b may be complex, the arguments giving the two phases. It is the general convention * to call the plane containing **H** and **n** the **plane of polarisation**. Thus (23) is a wave polarised in the xz plane, and (24) a wave polarised in the yz plane. By the principle of superposition (§ **6**) we may superpose solutions of types (23) and (24). If the two phases are different, we obtain **elliptically polarised light,** in which the end-point of the vector **E** describes an ellipse in the xy plane. If the phases are the same, we obtain **plane polarised light**, polarised in the plane $y/x = -b/a$. If the phases differ by $\pi/2$, and the amplitudes are equal, we obtain **circularly polarised light**, which, in real form, may be written

$$
\begin{aligned}
E_x &= a \cos p(t-z/V) & H_x &= -\sqrt{(\epsilon/\mu)}\, a \sin p(t-z/V) \\
E_y &= a \sin p(t-z/V) & H_y &= +\sqrt{(\epsilon/\mu)}\, a \cos p(t-z/V) \\
E_z &= 0 & H_z &= 0.
\end{aligned}
\tag{25}
$$

The end-points of the vectors **E** and **H** each describe circles in the xy plane.

In all three cases (23)-(25), when we are dealing with free space ($\epsilon = \mu = 1$) the magnitudes of **E** and **H** are equal.

§ **72.** By the use of (10) we can easily write down the rate at which energy is transmitted in these waves. Thus,

---

* To which, unfortunately, not all writers conform.

with (25) the Poynting Vector is simply $\left(0, \; 0, \; \dfrac{ca^2}{4\pi}\sqrt{\dfrac{\epsilon}{\mu}}\right)$.
This vector is in the direction of the positive z-axis, showing that energy is propagated with the waves. According to (9), the total energy per unit volume is

$$\frac{1}{8\pi}\{\epsilon\mathbf{E}^2 + \mu\mathbf{H}^2\} = \frac{1}{4\pi}\,\epsilon a^2.$$

From these two expressions we can deduce the velocity with which the energy flows; for this velocity is merely the ratio of the total flow across unit area in unit time divided by the energy per unit volume. This is $c/\sqrt{(\epsilon\mu)}$, so that the energy flows with the same velocity as the wave. This does not hold with all types of wave motion; an exception has already occurred in liquids (§ 52).

When we calculate the Poynting Vector for the waves (23) and (24), we must remember that $\dfrac{c}{4\pi}\,\mathbf{E}\times\mathbf{H}$ is not a linear function and consequently (see § 10) we must choose either the real or the imaginary parts of $\mathbf{E}$ and $\mathbf{H}$. Taking, for example, the real part of (23), the Poynting Vector lies in the z direction, with magnitude

$$\sqrt{\frac{\epsilon}{\mu}} \cdot \frac{c}{4\pi}\,a^2\cos^2 p\left(t - \frac{z}{V}\right),$$

This is a fluctuating quantity whose mean value with respect to the time is $\dfrac{ca^2}{8\pi}\sqrt{\dfrac{\epsilon}{\mu}}$. The energy density, from (9), is $\dfrac{\epsilon a^2}{4\pi}\cos^2 p(t - z/V)$, with a corresponding mean value $\epsilon a^2/8\pi$. Once again the velocity of transmission of energy is $\dfrac{ca^2}{8\pi}\sqrt{\dfrac{\epsilon}{\mu}} \div \dfrac{\epsilon a^2}{8\pi} = c/\sqrt{(\epsilon\mu)}$, which is the same as the wave velocity.

§ 73. We shall next discuss the reflection and refraction of plane harmonic light waves. This reflection will be supposed to take place at a plane surface separating two non-conducting dielectric media whose refractive indices are K_1 and K_2. Since we may put $\mu_1 = \mu_2 = 1$, the velocities in the two media are c/K_1, c/K_2. In fig. 21 let Oz be the

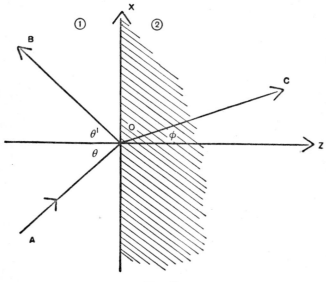

Fig. 21

direction of the common normal to the two media, and let AO, OB, OC be the directions of the incident, reflected and refracted (or transmitted) waves. We have not yet shown that these all lie in a plane; let us suppose that they make angles θ, $\pi - \theta'$ and ϕ with the z axis, OA being in the plane of the paper, and let us take the plane of incidence (i.e. the plane containing OA and Oz) to be the xz plane. The y axis is then perpendicular to the plane of the paper.

H

Since the angle of incidence is θ, then as in (20), each of the three components of **E** and **H** will be proportional to

$$e^{ip\{ct - K_1(x \sin \theta + z \cos \theta)\}}.$$

Let the reflected and transmitted rays move in directions (l_1, m_1, n_1) and (l_2, m_2, n_2) respectively so that $n_1 = -\cos \theta'$, $n_2 = \cos \phi$. Then the corresponding components of **E** and **H** for these rays will be proportional to

$$e^{ip\{ct - K_1(l_1 x + m_1 y + n_1 z)\}} \text{ and } e^{ip\{ct - K_2(l_2 x + m_2 y + n_2 z)\}}.$$

Thus, considering the E_x components, we may write the incident, reflected and transmitted values

$$A e^{ip\{ct - K_1(x \sin \theta + z \cos \theta)\}} , \quad A_1 e^{ip\{ct - K_1(l_1 x + m_1 y + n_1 z)\}} \quad \text{and}$$
$$A_2 e^{ip\{ct - K_2(l_2 x + m_2 y + n_2 z)\}}.$$

These functions all satisfy the standard equation of wave motion and they have the same frequency, a condition which is necessary from the very nature of the problem.

We shall first show that the reflected and transmitted waves lie in the plane of incidence. This follows from the boundary condition (8) that E_x must be continuous on the plane $z = 0$, i.e. for all x, y, t,

$$A e^{ip(ct - K_1 x \sin \theta)} + A_1 e^{ip\{ct - K_1(l_1 x + m_1 y)\}} = A_2 e^{ip\{ct - K_2(l_2 x + m_2 y)\}}.$$

This identity is only possible if the indices of all three terms are identical : i.e.

$$ct - K_1 x \sin \theta \equiv ct - K_1(l_1 x + m_1 y) \equiv ct - K_2(l_2 x + m_2 y).$$

Thus
$$K_1 \sin \theta = K_1 l_1 = K_2 l_2,$$
$$0 = K_1 m_1 = K_2 m_2.$$

The second of these relations shows that $m_1 = m_2 = 0$, so that the reflected and transmitted rays OB, OC lie in the plane of incidence xOz. The first relation shows that $l_1 = \sin \theta$, i.e. that the angle of reflection θ' is equal to the angle of incidence θ, and also that

$$K_1 \sin \theta = K_2 \sin \phi \quad . \quad . \quad . \quad (26)$$

This well-known relationship between the angles of incidence and refraction is known as **Snell's law.**

Our discussion so far has merely concerned itself with directions, and we must now pass to the amplitudes of the waves. There are two main cases to consider, according as the incident light is polarised in the plane of incidence, or perpendicular to it.

Incident light polarised in the plane of incidence.—The incident ray *AO* has its magnetic vector in the *xz* plane, directed perpendicular to *AO*. To express this vector in terms of *x*, *y*, *z* it is convenient to use intermediary axes ξ, η, ζ through *O* (see fig. 22, where the directions of ξ and ζ are shown; η coincides with the *y* axis which is

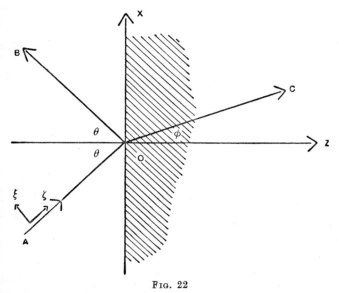

Fig. 22

perpendicular to the plane of the paper). ζ is in the direction of propagation, and ξ is in the plane of incidence. Referred to these new axes, **H** lies entirely in the ξ direction, and **E** in the η direction. We may use (23) and write

$$E_\xi = E_\zeta = 0 \, , \; E_\eta = a_1 e^{ip(ct - K_1\zeta)},$$
$$H_\eta = H_\zeta = 0 \, , \; H_\xi = -K_1 a_1 e^{ip(ct - K_1\zeta)}.$$

Now $\zeta = x \sin \theta + z \cos \theta$, and so it follows that :
incident wave

$$E_x = 0 \, , \quad H_x = -K_1 a_1 \cos \theta \; e^{ip\{ct - K_1(x \sin \theta + z \cos \theta)\}},$$
$$E_y = a_1 e^{ip\{ct - K_1(x \sin \theta + z \cos \theta)\}}, \quad H_y = 0,$$
$$E_z = 0 \, , \quad H_z = K_1 a_1 \sin \theta \; e^{ip\{ct - K_1(x \sin \theta + z \cos \theta)\}}.$$

Similar analysis for the reflected and refracted waves, in which we replace θ by $\pi - \theta$ and ϕ in turn, enables us to write

reflected wave

$$E_x = 0 \, , \quad H_x = K_1 b_1 \cos \theta \; e^{ip\{ct - K_1(x \sin \theta - z \cos \theta)\}},$$
$$E_y = b_1 e^{ip\{ct - K_1(x \sin \theta - z \cos \theta)\}}, \quad H_y = 0,$$
$$E_z = 0 \, , \quad H_z = K_1 b_1 \sin \theta \; e^{ip\{ct - K_1(x \sin \theta - z \cos \theta)\}} :$$

refracted wave

$$E_x = 0 \, , \quad H_x = -K_2 a_2 \cos \phi \; e^{ip\{ct - K_2(x \sin \phi + z \cos \phi)\}},$$
$$E_y = a_2 e^{ip\{ct - K_2(x \sin \phi + z \cos \phi)\}}, \quad H_y = 0,$$
$$E_z = 0 \, , \quad H_z = K_2 a_2 \sin \phi \; e^{ip\{ct - K_2(x \sin \phi + z \cos \phi)\}}.$$

We may write the boundary conditions in the form that E_x, E_y, $K^2 E_z$, H_x, H_y and H_z are continuous at $z = 0$. These six conditions reduce to two independent relations, which we may take to be those due to E_y and H_x :

$$a_1 + b_1 = a_2,$$
$$-K_1 a_1 \cos \theta + K_1 b_1 \cos \theta = -K_2 a_2 \cos \phi.$$

Thus

$$\frac{a_1}{K_1 \cos \theta + K_2 \cos \phi} = \frac{b_1}{K_1 \cos \theta - K_2 \cos \phi} = \frac{a_2}{2K_1 \cos \theta}.$$

Using Snell's law (26) in the form $K_1 : K_2 = \sin \phi : \sin \theta$, this gives

$$\frac{a_1}{\sin (\theta + \phi)} = \frac{b_1}{-\sin (\theta - \phi)} = \frac{a_2}{2 \sin \phi \cos \theta}. \tag{27}$$

Equation (27) gives the ratio of the reflected and refracted amplitudes. If medium 2 is denser than medium 1, $K_2 > K_1$, so that $\theta > \phi$, and thus b_1/a_1 is negative ; so there is a phase change of π in the electric field when reflection takes place in the lighter medium. There is no phase change on reflection in a denser medium, nor in the refracted wave. The same conclusion is true for the magnetic field **H**, though it must be remembered here and later in this chapter that the positive directions for **E** and **H** are defined by $\xi\eta\zeta$ in fig. 22 and their counterparts relative to OB, OC, the η direction being along the y axis throughout.

Incident light polarised perpendicular to the plane of incidence.—A similar discussion can be given when the incident light is polarised perpendicular to the plane of incidence ; in this case the rôles of **E** and **H** are practically interchanged, H_y for example being the only non-vanishing component of **H**. It is not necessary to repeat the analysis in full. With the same notation for the amplitudes of the incident, reflected and refracted waves, we have

$$\frac{a_1}{\sin 2\theta + \sin 2\phi} = \frac{b_1}{\sin 2\theta - \sin 2\phi} = \frac{a_2}{4 \cos \theta \sin \phi} . \quad (28)$$

It follows from (28) that the reflected ray vanishes if $\sin 2\theta = \sin 2\phi$. Since $\theta \neq \phi$, this implies that $\theta + \phi = \pi/2$, and then Snell's law gives

$$K_1 \sin \theta = K_2 \sin \phi = K_2 \cos \theta,$$

So

$$\tan \theta = K_2/K_1 = \sqrt{(\epsilon_2/\epsilon_1)} \quad . \quad . \quad (29)$$

With this angle of incidence, known as **Brewster's angle,** there is no reflected ray.

There will be a phase change of π in **E** on reflection when $\sin 2\theta < \sin 2\phi$. If reflection takes place in the lighter medium so that $K_1 < K_2$, this holds for θ greater than Brewster's angle ; but if $K_1 > K_2$ it holds for θ less than Brewster's angle. In all other cases there is no phase change on reflection.

In general, of course, the incident light is composed of waves polarised in all possible directions. Equations (27) and (28) show that if the original amplitudes in the two main directions are equal, the reflected amplitudes will not be equal, so that the light becomes partly polarised on reflection. When the angle of incidence is given by (29) it is completely polarised on reflection. This angle is therefore sometimes known as the **polarising angle**.

§ 74. An interesting possibility arises in the discussion of § 73, which gives rise to the phenomenon known as **total** or **internal reflection**. It arises when reflection takes place in the denser medium so that $\phi > \theta$. If we suppose θ to be steadily increased from zero, then ϕ also increases and when $\sin \theta = K_2/K_1$, $\phi = \pi/2$. If θ is increased beyond this critical value, ϕ is imaginary. There is nothing to disturb us in this fact provided that we interpret the analysis of § 73 correctly, for we never had occasion to suppose that the coefficients were real. We can easily make the necessary adjustment in this case. Take for simplicity the case of incident light polarised in the plane of incidence. Then the incident and reflected waves are just as in our previous calculations. The refracted wave has the same form also, but in the exponential term, $K_2 \sin \phi = K_1 \sin \theta$, and is therefore real, whereas

$$K_2 \cos \phi = \sqrt{(K_2{}^2 - K_2{}^2 \sin^2 \phi)} = \sqrt{(K_2{}^2 - K_1{}^2 \sin^2 \theta)},$$

and is imaginary, since we are supposing that internal reflection is taking place and therefore $K_1 \sin \theta > K_2$. We may therefore write $K_2 \cos \phi = \pm iq$, where q is real. Thus the refracted wave has the form

$$E_y = a_2 e^{ip(ct - K_1 \sin\theta\, x \pm iqz)}$$
$$= a_2 e^{\pm pqz} e^{ip(ct - K_1 \sin\theta\, x)}.$$

For reasons of finiteness at infinity, we have to choose the negative sign, so that it appears that the wave is attenuated as it proceeds into the less dense medium.

For normal light waves it appears that the penetration is only a few wavelengths, and this justifies the title of total reflection. The decay factor is

$$e^{-pqz} = e^{-p\sqrt{(K_1^2 \sin^2 \theta - K_2^2)}z}.$$

This factor increases with the frequency so that light of great frequency hardly penetrates at all. In actual physical problems, the refractive index does not change from K_1 to K_2 abruptly, as we have imagined; however, Drude has shown that if we suppose that there is a thin surface layer, of thickness approximately equal to one atomic diameter, in which the change takes place smoothly, the results of this and the preceding paragraphs are hardly affected.

§ 75. In our previous calculations we have assumed that the medium was non-conducting, so that we could put $\sigma = 0$. When we remove this restriction, keeping always to homogeneous media, equations (1)-(7) give us

$$\operatorname{div} \mathbf{E} = 0,$$
$$\operatorname{div} \mathbf{H} = 0,$$
$$\operatorname{curl} \mathbf{H} = 4\pi\sigma\mathbf{E} + \frac{\epsilon}{c}\frac{\partial \mathbf{E}}{\partial t},$$
$$\operatorname{curl} \mathbf{E} = -\frac{\mu}{c}\frac{\partial \mathbf{H}}{\partial t}.$$

Now curl curl $\mathbf{E} = \operatorname{grad} \operatorname{div} \mathbf{E} - \nabla^2\mathbf{E} = -\nabla^2\mathbf{E}$, so that

$$\nabla^2\mathbf{E} = \frac{\mu}{c}\operatorname{curl}\frac{\partial \mathbf{H}}{\partial t} = \frac{\mu}{c}\frac{\partial}{\partial t}\operatorname{curl}\mathbf{H} = \frac{4\pi\sigma\mu}{c}\frac{\partial \mathbf{E}}{\partial t} + \frac{\epsilon\mu}{c^2}\frac{\partial^2\mathbf{E}}{\partial t^2},$$

i.e.
$$\nabla^2\mathbf{E} = \frac{\epsilon\mu}{c^2}\frac{\partial^2\mathbf{E}}{\partial t^2} + \frac{4\pi\sigma\mu}{c}\frac{\partial \mathbf{E}}{\partial t} \quad . \quad . \quad (30)$$

A similar equation holds for $\mathbf{H}$. Equation (30) is the well-known equation of telegraphy (see § 9). The first term on the right-hand side may be called the displacement term, since it arises from the displacement current $\dfrac{1}{4\pi c}\dfrac{\partial \mathbf{D}}{\partial t}$

and the second is the conduction term, since it arises from the conduction current $\mathbf{j}$. If we are dealing with waves whose frequency is $p/2\pi$, $\mathbf{E}$ will be proportional to e^{ipt}; the ratio of these two terms is therefore $\epsilon p/4\pi c\sigma$. Since ϵ is generally of the order of unity, this means that if $p/2\pi$ is much greater than $c\sigma$, only the displacement term matters (this is the case of light waves in a non-conducting dielectric); but if $p/2\pi$ is much less than $c\sigma$, only the conduction term matters (this is the case of long waves in a good metallic conductor). In the intermediate region both terms must be retained. With most metals, if $p < 10^7$ per second we can neglect the first term, and if $p > 10^{15}$ per second we can neglect the second term.

Let us discuss the solutions of (30) which apply to plane harmonic waves propagated in the z direction, such that only E_x and H_y are non-vanishing (as in (24)). We may suppose that each of these components is proportional to

$$e^{ip(t-qz)} \qquad . \qquad . \qquad . \qquad . \qquad (31)$$

where $p/2\pi$ is the frequency and q is still to be determined. This expression satisfies the equation (30) if

$$q^2 = \frac{\epsilon\mu}{c^2}\left\{1 - \frac{4\pi\sigma c}{\epsilon p} i\right\} \qquad . \qquad . \qquad (32)$$

q is therefore complex, and we may write it

$$q = \alpha - i\beta,$$

where

$$\alpha^2 = \frac{\epsilon\mu}{2c^2}\left[\left\{1 + \left(\frac{4\pi\sigma c}{\epsilon p}\right)^2\right\}^{1/2} + 1\right]$$

$$\beta^2 = \frac{\epsilon\mu}{2c^2}\left[\left\{1 + \left(\frac{4\pi\sigma c}{\epsilon p}\right)^2\right\}^{1/2} - 1\right] \qquad . \qquad (33)$$

The "velocity" of (31) is $1/q$; but we have seen in § **73** that in a medium of refractive index K the velocity is c/K. So the effective refractive index is cq which is complex. Complex refractive indices occur quite frequently and are

associated with absorption of the waves; for, combining
(31) and (33) we have the result that E_x and H_y are
proportional to

$$e^{-p\beta z}e^{ip(t-az)} \qquad . \qquad . \qquad . \qquad (34)$$

This shows that a plane wave cannot be propagated in
such a medium without absorption. The decay factor may
be written e^{-kz} where $k = p\beta$. k is called the **absorption
coefficient.** In the case where $4\pi\sigma c/\epsilon p$ is small compared
with unity (the case of light waves in most non-conducting
dielectrics), k is approximately equal to $2\pi\sigma\sqrt{(\mu/\epsilon)}$. Now
the wavelength in (34) is $\lambda = 2\pi/ap$, so that in one wavelength the amplitude decays by a factor $e^{-k\lambda}$, approximately
$e^{-4\pi^2\sigma c/\epsilon p}$. As we are making the assumption that $c\sigma/\epsilon p$
is small, the decay is gradual, and can only be noticed
after many wavelengths. The distance travelled before
the amplitude is reduced to $1/e$ times its original value is
$1/k$, which is of the same order as σ.

The velocity of propagation of (34) is $1/a$, and thus
varies with the frequency. With our usual approximation
that $c\sigma/\epsilon p$ is small, this velocity is

$$\frac{c}{\sqrt{(\epsilon\mu)}}\left\{1 - \frac{1}{2}\left(\frac{2\pi\sigma c}{\epsilon p}\right)^2\right\}. \qquad . \qquad . \qquad (35)$$

We can show that in waves of this character **E** and **H**
are out of phase with each other. For if, in accordance
with (31), we write

$$E_x = a\ e^{ip(t-qz)},$$
$$H_y = b\ e^{ip(t-qz)},$$

then the y-component of the vector relation

$$\text{curl } \mathbf{E} = -\frac{\mu}{c}\frac{\partial \mathbf{H}}{\partial t},$$

gives us the connection between a and b. It is

$$\frac{\partial E_x}{\partial z} = -\frac{\mu}{c}\frac{\partial H_y}{\partial t},$$

i.e.
$$qa = \frac{\mu}{c} b \qquad . \quad . \quad . \quad . \quad (36)$$

Thus b/a is equal to $(c/\mu)q$. Now q is complex and hence there is a phase difference between E_x and H_y equal to the argument of q. This is $\tan^{-1}(\beta/a)$, and with the same approximation as in (35), this is just $\tan^{-1}(2\pi\sigma c/\epsilon p)$, which is effectively $2\pi\sigma c/\epsilon p$.

§ 76. It is interesting to discuss in more detail the case in which the conductivity is so great that we may completely neglect the displacement term in (30). Let us consider the case of a beam of light falling normally on an infinite metallic conductor bounded by the plane $z = 0$. Let us suppose (fig. 23) that the incident waves

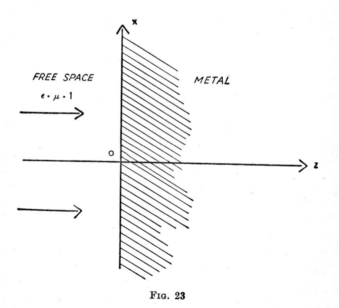

FREE SPACE
$\epsilon \cdot \mu \cdot 1$

METAL

Fig. 23

come from the negative direction of z, in free space, for which $\epsilon = \mu = 1$, and are polarised in the yz plane. Then, according to (24) they are defined by :

incident wave

$$E_x = a_1\, e^{ip(t-z/c)} \quad,\quad H_y = a_1\, e^{ip(t-z/c)}.$$

reflected wave

$$E_x = b_1\, e^{ip(t+z/c)} \quad,\quad H_y = -b_1\, e^{ip(t+z/c)}.$$

In the metal itself we may write, according to (31) and (36),

$$E_x = a_2\, e^{ip(t-qz)} \quad,\quad H_y = \frac{c}{\mu}\, q\, a_2\, e^{ip(t-qz)}.$$

These values will satisfy the equation of telegraphy (30) in which we have neglected the displacement term, if

$$q^2 = -\frac{4\pi\sigma\mu}{pc}\, i = -2\gamma^2 i,$$

where $\gamma^2 = 2\pi\sigma\mu/pc.$ Thus

$$q = \gamma(1-i). \quad .\quad .\quad .\quad .\quad .\quad .\quad (37)$$

Inside the metal, **E** and **H** have a $\pi/4$ phase difference, since, as we have shown in (36), this phase difference is merely the argument of q.

The boundary conditions are that E_x and H_y are continuous at $z = 0$. This gives two equations

$$a_1 + b_1 = a_2,$$

$$a_1 - b_1 = \frac{c}{\mu}\, q a_2.$$

Hence

$$\frac{a_1}{1+\dfrac{c}{\mu}q} = \frac{b_1}{1-\dfrac{c}{\mu}q} = \frac{a_2}{2}. \quad .\quad .\quad (38)$$

Since q is complex, all three electric vectors have phase differences. The ratio R of reflected to incident energy is $|b_1/a_1|^2$, which reduces to

$$\frac{(c\gamma-\mu)^2 + (c\gamma)^2}{(c\gamma+\mu)^2 + (c\gamma)^2}.$$

In the case of non-ferromagnetic metals, $c\gamma$ is much larger than μ, so that approximately

$$R = 1 - \frac{2\mu}{c\gamma}.$$

This formula has been checked excellently by the experiments of Hagen and Rubens, using wavelengths in the region of 10^{-5} cms.

It is an easy matter to generalise these results to apply to the case when we include both the displacement and conduction terms in (30).

We can use (38) to calculate the loss of energy in the metal. If we consider unit area of the surface of the metal, the rate of arrival of energy is given by the Poynting Vector. This is $\frac{c}{8\pi} |a_1|^2$. Similarly the rate of reflection of energy is $\frac{c}{8\pi} |b_1|^2$. So the rate of dissipation is $\frac{c}{8\pi} \left\{ |a_1|^2 - |b_1|^2 \right\}$.

This must be the same as the Joule heat loss. In our units, this loss is $c\sigma E^2$ per unit volume per unit time. If we take the mean value of E_x^2 in the metal, it is an easy matter to show that $\int_0^\infty c\sigma E_x^2 dz$ is indeed exactly equal to this rate of dissipation.

§ 77. When the radiation falls on the metal of § 76, it exerts a pressure. We may calculate this, if we use the experimental law that when a current **j** is in the presence of a magnetic field **H** there is a force $\mu \mathbf{j} \times \mathbf{H}$ acting on it. In our problem, there is, in the metal, an alternating field **E**, and a corresponding current $\sigma \mathbf{E}$. The force on the current is therefore $\mu\sigma \mathbf{E} \times \mathbf{H}$, and this force, being perpendicular to **E** and **H**, lies in the z direction. The force on the charges that compose the current is transmitted by them to the metal as a whole. Now both **E** and **H** are proportional to $e^{-p\gamma z}$ (see equation 37) so that the force falls off according to the relation $e^{-2p\gamma z}$. To calculate the total force on unit area of the metal surface, we must integrate $\mu\sigma\mathbf{E}\times\mathbf{H}$ from $z = 0$ to $z = \infty$. $\mathbf{E}\times\mathbf{H}$ is a fluctuating quantity, and so we shall have to take its mean value with respect to the time. The pressure is then

$$\mu\sigma \cdot \frac{c}{\mu} \mid a_2 \mid^2 \int_0^\infty \frac{1}{2}\, \gamma e^{-2p\gamma z} dz,$$

i.e.
$$(c\sigma/4p) \mid a_2 \mid^2.$$

Using (38) this may be expressed in the form
$$(c\sigma\mu^2/p) \mid a_1 \mid^2 \{(c\gamma+\mu)^2+(c\gamma)^2\}^{-1}.$$

§ **78**. There is another application of the theory of § **76** which is important. Suppose that we have a straight wire of circular section, and a rapidly alternating e.m.f. is applied at its two ends. We have seen in § **76** that with an infinite sheet of metal the current falls off as we penetrate the metal according to the law $e^{-p\gamma z}$. If $p\gamma$ is small, there is little diminution as we go down a distance equal to the radius of the wire, and clearly the current will be almost constant for all parts of any section (see, however, question (12) in § **79**). But if $p\gamma$ is large, then the current will be carried mainly near the surface of the wire, and it will not make a great deal of difference whether the metal is infinite in extent, as we supposed in § **76**, or whether it has a cross-section in the form of a circle ; in this case the current density falls off approximately according to the law $e^{-p\gamma r}$ as we go down a distance r from the surface. This phenomenon is known as the **skin effect** ; it is more pronounced at very high frequencies.

We could of course solve the problem of the wire quite rigorously, using cylindrical polar coordinates. The formulæ are rather complicated, but the result is essentially the same.

§ 79.   Examples

(1) Prove the equations (17′) and (18′) in § 70.

(2) Find the value of **H** when $E_x = E_y = 0$, and $E_z = A \cos nx \cos nct$. It is given that **H** = 0 when $t = 0$, and also $\epsilon = \mu = 1$, $\rho = \sigma = 0$. Show that there is no mean flux of energy in this problem.

(3) Prove the equation (28) in § 73 for reflection and refraction of light polarised perpendicular to the plane of incidence.

(4) Show that the polarising angle is less than the critical angle for internal reflection. Calculate the two values if $K_1 = 6$, $K_2 = 1$.

(5) Show that the reflection coefficient from glass to air at normal incidence is the same as from air to glass, but that the two phase changes are different.

(6) Light falls normally on the plane face which separates two media K_1, K_2. Show that a fraction R of the energy is reflected, and T is transmitted, where

$$R = \left(\frac{K_2 - K_1}{K_2 + K_1}\right)^2 \ , \ T = \frac{4K_1 K_2}{(K_2 + K_1)^2}.$$

Hence prove that if light falls normally on a slab of dielectric, bounded by two parallel faces, the total fraction of energy reflected is $\dfrac{(K_2 - K_1)^2}{K_1^2 + K_2^2}$, and transmitted is $\dfrac{2K_1 K_2}{K_1^2 + K_2^2}$. It is necessary to take account of the multiple reflections that take place at each boundary.

(7) Light passes normally through the two parallel faces of a piece of plate glass, for which $K = 1 \cdot 5$. Find the fraction of incident energy transmitted, taking account of reflection at the faces.

(8) Show that when internal reflection (§ 74) is taking place, there is a phase change in the reflected beam. Evaluate this numerically for the case of a beam falling at an angle of 60° to the normal when $K_1 = 1 \cdot 6$, $K_2 = 1$, the light being polarised in the plane of incidence.

(9) Show that if $\mu = 1$, then the reflection coefficient with metals (§ 76) may be written in the form $R = 1 - 2/\sqrt{(c\sigma/\nu)}$,

where ν is the frequency. If σ is $1\cdot6 \,.\, 10^7$ (in our mixed units), calculate R for $\lambda = 10^{-3}$ cms. and $\lambda = 10^{-4}$ cms.

(10) A current flows in a straight wire whose cross-section is a circle of radius a. The conduction current $\mathbf{j}$ depends only on r the radial distance from the centre of the wire, and the time t. Assuming that the displacement current can be neglected, prove that $\mathbf{H}$ is directed perpendicular to the radius vector. If $j(r, t)$ and $H(r, t)$ represent the magnitudes of $\mathbf{j}$ and $\mathbf{H}$, prove that

$$\frac{\partial}{\partial r}(Hr) = 4\pi rj \,,\; \frac{\partial j}{\partial r} = \frac{\mu\sigma}{c}\frac{\partial H}{\partial t}.$$

(11) Use the results of question (10) to prove that j satisfies the differential equation

$$\frac{1}{r}\frac{\partial}{\partial r}\left(r\frac{\partial j}{\partial r}\right) = \frac{4\pi\sigma\mu}{c}\frac{\partial j}{\partial t}.$$

By using the formula for curl in cylindrical polars twice in succession show that $H[= H_\theta(r, t)]$ satisfies the equation

$$\frac{\partial^2 H}{\partial r^2} + \frac{1}{r}\frac{\partial H}{\partial r} - \frac{H}{r^2} = [\text{curl curl } \mathbf{H}]_\theta = \frac{4\pi\mu\sigma}{c}\frac{\partial H}{\partial t}.$$

Use the method of separation of variables to prove that there is a solution of the j-equation of the form $j = f(r)e^{ipt}$, where

$$\frac{d^2f}{dr^2} + \frac{1}{r}\frac{df}{dr} - 4iaf = 0 \,,\; a = \pi\sigma\mu p/c.$$

Hence show that f is a combination of Bessel functions of order zero and complex argument.

(12) If a in question (11) is small, show that an approximate solution of the current equation is $j = A(1+iar^2-\tfrac{1}{4}a^2r^4)e^{ipt}$, where A is a constant. Hence show that the total current fluctuates between $\pm J$, where, neglecting powers of a above the second, $J = \pi a^2 A(1+a^4a^2/24)$. Use this result to show that the heat developed in unit length of the wire in unit time is $\dfrac{cJ^2}{2\pi\sigma a^2}\,(1+a^4a^2/12)$. (Questions (10), (11) and (12) are the problem of the skin effect at low frequencies.)

[ANSWERS: 2. $H_x = H_z = 0$, $H_y = -A\sin nx \sin nct$; 4. $9°\,28'$, $9°\,36'$; 7. 12/13 of the incident energy is transmitted ; 8. $100°\,20'$; 9. $0\cdot984$, $0\cdot950$.]

CHAPTER VIII

GENERAL CONSIDERATIONS

§ 80. The speed at which waves travel in a medium is usually independent of the velocity of the source; thus, if a pebble is thrown into a pond with a horizontal velocity, the waves travel radially outwards from the centre of disturbance in the form of concentric circles, with a speed which is independent of the velocity of the pebble that caused them.

When we have a moving source, sending out waves continuously as it moves, the velocity of the waves is often unchanged,* but the wavelength and frequency, as noted by a stationary observer, may be altered.

Thus, consider a source of waves moving towards an observer with velocity u. Then, since the source is moving,

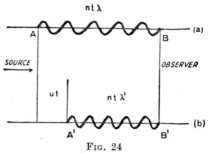

FIG. 24

(a) Waves when source is stationary.
(b) Waves when source is moving.

the waves which are between the source and the observer will be crowded into a smaller distance than if the source had been at rest. This is shown in fig. 24, where the waves are drawn both for a stationary and a moving source. If the frequency is n, then in time t the source emits nt waves.

* It is changed slightly when there is dispersion; see § 83.

If the source had been at rest, these waves would have occupied a length AB. But due to its motion the source has covered a distance ut, and hence these nt waves are compressed into a length $A'B'$, where $AB - A'B' = ut$. Thus

$$nt\lambda - nt\lambda' = ut,$$

i.e. $$\lambda' = \lambda - u/n = \lambda(1 - u/c), \quad . \quad . \quad . \quad (1)$$

if c is the wave velocity. If the corresponding frequencies measured by the fixed observer are n and n', then, since $n\lambda = c = n'\lambda'$, therefore

$$n' = \frac{nc}{c - u} \quad . \quad . \quad . \quad (2)$$

If the source is moving towards the observer the frequency is increased ; if it moves away from him, the frequency is decreased. This explains the sudden change of pitch noticed by a stationary observer when a motor-car passes him. The actual change in this case is from $nc/(c-u)$ to $nc/(c+u)$, so that

$$\Delta n = 2ncu/(c^2 - u^2). \quad . \quad . \quad (3)$$

This phenomenon of the change of frequency when a source is moving is known as the **Doppler effect**. It applies equally well if the observer is moving instead of the source, or if both are moving.

For, consider the case of the observer moving with velocity v away from the source, which is supposed to be at rest. Let us superimpose upon the whole motion, observer, source and waves, a velocity $-v$. We shall then have a situation in which the observer is at rest, the source has a velocity $-v$, and the waves travel with a speed $c-v$. We may apply equation (2) which will then give the appropriate frequency as registered by the observer; if this is n'', then

$$n'' = \frac{n(c-v)}{(c-v) - (-v)} = \frac{n(c-v)}{c} \quad . \quad . \quad (4)$$

I

To deal with the case in which both source and observer are moving, with velocities u and v respectively, in the same direction, we superimpose again a velocity $-v$ upon the whole motion. Then in the new problem, the observer is at rest, the source has a velocity $u-v$, and the waves travel with velocity $c-v$. Again, we may apply (2) and if the frequency registered by the observer is n''', we have

$$n''' = \frac{n(c-v)}{(c-v) - (u-v)} = \frac{n(c-v)}{c-u} \qquad . \qquad (5)$$

These considerations are of importance in acoustic and optical problems; it is not difficult to extend them to deal with cases in which the various velocities are not in the same line, but we shall not discuss such problems here.

§ 81. We have shown in Chapter I, § 6 that we may superpose any number of separate solutions of the wave equation. Suppose that we have two harmonic solutions (Chapter I, equation (11)) with equal amplitudes and nearly equal frequencies. Then the total disturbance is

$$\phi = a \cos 2\pi(k_1 x - n_1 t) + a \cos 2\pi(k_2 x - n_2 t)$$
$$= 2a \cos 2\pi\left\{\frac{k_1 + k_2}{2} x - \frac{n_1 + n_2}{2} t\right\} \cos 2\pi\left\{\frac{k_1 - k_2}{2} x - \frac{n_1 - n_2}{2} t\right\} \quad (6)$$

The first cosine factor represents a wave very similar to the original waves, whose frequency and wavelength are an average of the two initial values, and which moves with a velocity $\frac{n_1 + n_2}{k_1 + k_2}$. This is practically the same as the velocity of the original waves, and is indeed exactly the same if $n_1/k_1 = n_2/k_2$. But the second cosine factor, which changes much more slowly both with respect to x and t, may be regarded as a varying amplitude. Thus, for the resultant of the two original waves, we have a wave of approximately the same wavelength and frequency, but with an amplitude that changes both with time and distance.

We may represent this graphically, as in fig. 25. The outer solid profile is the curve

$$y = 2a \cos 2\pi \left\{ \frac{k_1 - k_2}{2} x - \frac{n_1 - n_2}{2} t \right\}.$$

The other profile curve is the reflection of this in the x axis. The actual disturbance ϕ lies between these two boundaries, cutting the axis of x at regular intervals, and touching alternately the upper and lower profile curves. If the velocities of the two component waves are the same, so that $n_1/k_1 = n_2/k_2$, then the wave system shown in fig. 25 moves steadily forward without change

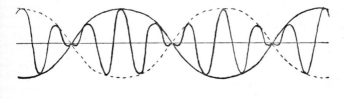

$\longrightarrow x$

Fig. 25

of shape. The case when n_1/k_1 is not equal to n_2/k_2 is dealt with in § 83.

Suppose that ϕ refers to sound waves. Then we shall hear a resultant wave whose frequency is the mean of the two original frequencies, but whose intensity fluctuates with a frequency *twice* that of the solid profile curve. This fluctuating intensity is known as **beats** ; its frequency, which is known as the **beat frequency**, is just $n_1 \sim n_2$, that is, the difference of the component frequencies. We can detect beats very easily with a piano slightly out of tune, or with two equal tuning-forks on the prongs of one of which we have put a little sealing wax to decrease its frequency. Determination of the beat frequency between a standard tuning-fork and an unknown frequency is one of the best methods of determining the unknown frequency. Low frequency beats are unpleasant to the ear.

§ **82.** There is another phenomenon closely related to beats. Let us suppose that we have a harmonic wave $\phi = A \cos 2\pi(nt - kx)$, with amplitude A and frequency n. Suppose further that the amplitude A is made to vary with the time in such a way that at $x = 0$, $A = a + b \cos 2\pi pt$. If the wave is to move with velocity $c = n/k$, ϕ must be some function of $ct - x$. So for general x, $A = a + b \cos 2\pi p(t - kx/n)$. This is known as **amplitude modulation.** The result is

$$\phi = \{a + b \cos 2\pi p(t - kx/n)\}\cos 2\pi(nt - kx)$$
$$= a \cos 2\pi(nt - kx)$$
$$+ \frac{b}{2}\left\{ \cos\left[2\pi(n+p)\left(t - \frac{kx}{n}\right)\right] + \cos\left[2\pi(n-p)\left(t - \frac{kx}{n}\right)\right]\right\}.$$

The effect of modulating, or varying, the amplitude, is to introduce two new frequencies as well as the original one ; these new frequencies $n \pm p$ are known as **combination tones.** In the same way we can discuss **phase modulation** and **frequency modulation.** (See § 89, questions (11)–(12).)

§ **83.** If the velocities of § 81 are not the same (n_1/k_1 not equal to n_2/k_2), then the profile curves in fig. 25 move with a speed $(n_1 - n_2)/(k_1 - k_2)$, which is different from that of the more rapidly oscillating part, whose speed is $(n_1 + n_2)/(k_1 + k_2)$. In other words, the individual waves in fig. 25 advance through the profile, gradually increasing and then decreasing their amplitude, as they give place to other succeeding waves. This explains why, on the seashore, a wave which looks very large when it is some distance away from the shore, gradually reduces in height as it moves in, and may even disappear before it is sufficiently close to break.

This situation arises whenever the velocity of the waves, i.e. their **wave velocity** V, is not constant, but depends on the frequency. This phenomenon is known as **dispersion**. We deduce that in a dispersive system the only wave profile that can be transmitted without change of shape is a single harmonic wave train ; any other wave profile, which may be analysed into two or more harmonic wave trains, will change as it is propagated. The actual velocity of the profile curves in fig. 25 is known as the **group velocity** U. We see from (6) that if the two components are not very different, $V = n/k$, and

$$U = (n_1 - n_2)/(k_1 - k_2) = dn/dk. \qquad (7)$$

In terms of the wavelength λ, we have $k = 1/\lambda$, so that

$$U = \frac{dn}{d(1/\lambda)} = -\lambda^2 \frac{dn}{d\lambda}. \qquad (8)$$

We could equally well write this

$$U = \frac{dn}{dk} = \frac{d(kV)}{dk} = V + k\frac{dV}{dk} = V - \lambda\frac{dV}{d\lambda}. \qquad (9)$$

Our calculation has considered just two waves. But the form of equation (7) shows that we could equally well consider any number of waves superposed, provided that for any two of them $n_1 - n_2$ and $k_1 - k_2$ were sufficiently small for us to take their ratio constant and equal to dn/dk. If this condition is not satisfied we have to go to a closer approximation, as in § 84.

The importance of group velocity lies in the fact that the energy is propagated with this velocity. We have already met several cases in which the wave velocity depends on the frequency ; we shall calculate the group velocity for three of them.

Surface waves on a liquid of depth h :

The analysis of Chapter V, equation (32) shows that the velocity of surface waves on a liquid of depth h is given by

$$V^2 = \frac{g\lambda}{2\pi} \tanh \frac{2\pi h}{\lambda}.$$

According to (9) therefore, the group velocity is $V - \lambda dV/d\lambda$,

i.e. $$U = \frac{1}{2} V \left\{ 1 + \frac{4\pi h}{\lambda} \operatorname{cosech} \frac{4\pi h}{\lambda} \right\} \qquad (10)$$

When h is small, the two velocities are almost the same, but when h is large, $U = V/2$, so that the group velocity for deep sea waves is one-half of the wave velocity. Equation (10) is the same as the expression obtained in § **52**, equation (47), for the rate of transmission of energy in these surface waves. Thus the energy is transmitted with the group velocity.

Electric waves in a dielectric medium :

The analysis in Chapter VII, § **69**, shows that the wave velocity in a dielectric medium is given by

$$V^2 = c^2/\epsilon\mu.$$

We may put $\mu = 1$ for waves in the visible region. Now the dielectric constant ϵ is not independent of the frequency, and so V depends on λ. The group velocity follows from (9) ; it is

$$U = V \left\{ 1 + \frac{\lambda}{2\epsilon} \frac{\partial\epsilon}{\partial\lambda} \right\} \qquad . \qquad . \qquad (11)$$

In most regions, especially when λ is long, ϵ decreases when λ increases so that U is less than V. For certain wavelengths, however, particularly those in the neighbourhood of a natural frequency of the atoms of the dielectric, there is **anomalous dispersion**, and U may exceed V. When λ is large, we have the approximate formula

$$\epsilon = A + B/\lambda^2 + C/\lambda^4.$$

It then appears from (11) that

$$U = V \frac{A - C/\lambda^4}{A + B_1\lambda^2 + C/\lambda^4}.$$

Electric waves in a conducting medium :

The analysis in Chapter VII, § **76**, shows that the electric vector is propagated with an exponential term $e^{ip(t-\gamma z)}$, where $\gamma^2 = 2\pi\sigma\mu/pc$. Thus $V^2 = \dfrac{1}{\gamma^2} = \dfrac{pc}{2\pi\sigma\mu}$. According to (7), the group velocity is

$$U = \frac{dp}{d(p\gamma)} = \frac{1}{\gamma + p\dfrac{d\gamma}{dp}}.$$

If we suppose that σ and μ remain constant for all frequencies, then this reduces to

$$U = 2/\gamma = 2V . \quad . \quad . \quad (12)$$

The group velocity here is actually greater than the wave velocity.

§ 84. We shall now extend this discussion of group velocity to deal with the case of more than two component waves. We shall suppose that the wave profile is split up into an infinite number of harmonic waves of the type

$$e^{2\pi i(kx - nt)}, \quad . \quad . \quad . \quad (13)$$

in which the wave number k has all possible values ; we can suppose that the wave velocity depends on the frequency, so that n is a function of k. If the amplitude of the component wave (13) is $a(k)$ per unit range of k, then the full disturbance is

$$\phi(x,\ t) = \int_{k\,=\,-\infty}^{k\,=\,\infty} a(k) \cdot e^{2\pi i(kx - nt)} dk \quad . \quad . \quad (14)$$

This collection of superposed waves is known as a **wave packet.** The most interesting wave packets are those in which the amplitude is largest for a certain value of k, say k_0, and is vanishingly small if $k - k_0$ is large. Then the component waves mostly resemble $e^{2\pi i(k_0 x - n_0 t)}$, and there are not many waves which differ greatly from this.

We shall discuss in detail the case in which

$$a(k) = A\ e^{-\sigma(k - k_0)^2}. \quad . \quad . \quad (15)$$

This is known as a **Gaussian wave packet,** after the mathematician Gauss, who used the exponential function (15) in many of his investigations of other problems. A, σ and k_0 are, of course, constants for any one packet.

Let us first determine the shape of the wave profile at $t = 0$. The integral in (14) is much simplified because the term in n disappears. In fact,

$$\phi(x, 0) = \int_{-\infty}^{\infty} A \ e^{-\sigma(k - k_0)^2} \cdot e^{2\pi i k x} \, dk.$$

On account of the term $e^{-\sigma(k-k_0)^2}$, the only range of k which contributes significantly to this integral lies around k_0; since when $k - k_0 = 1/\sqrt{\sigma}$ this term becomes e^{-1}, and for larger values of $k - k_0$ it becomes rapidly smaller, this range of k is of order of magnitude $\Delta k = 1/\sqrt{\sigma}$.

In order to evaluate the integral, we use the result *

$$\int_{-\infty}^{+\infty} e^{au - bu^2} du = e^{\frac{a^2}{4b}} \int_{-\infty}^{+\infty} e^{-b\left(u^2 - \frac{a}{b}u + \frac{a^2}{4b^2}\right)} du$$

$$= e^{\frac{a^2}{4b}} \int_{-\infty}^{+\infty} e^{-bv^2} dv = \sqrt{\frac{\pi}{b}} \, e^{a^2/4b}. \quad \cdot \quad (17)$$

This enables us to integrate at once, and we find that

$$\phi(x, 0) = A \sqrt{\frac{\pi}{\sigma}} \ e^{-\pi^2 x^2/\sigma} \ e^{2\pi i k_0 x}. \quad \cdot \quad (18)$$

The term $e^{2\pi i k_0 x}$ represents a harmonic wave, whose

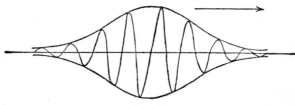

Fig. 26

wavelength $\lambda = 1/k_0$, and the other factors give a varying amplitude $A \sqrt{\frac{\pi}{\sigma}} \, e^{-\pi^2 x^2/\sigma}$. If we take the real part of (18),

* Gillespie, *Integration*, p. 88.

$\phi(x, 0)$ has the general shape shown in fig. 26. The outer curves in this figure are the two Gaussian curves

$$y = \pm A \sqrt{\frac{\pi}{\sigma}} e^{-\pi^2 x^2/\sigma},$$

and $\phi(x, 0)$ oscillates between them. Our wave packet (14) represents, at $t = 0$, one large pulse containing several oscillations. If we define a **half-width** as the value of x that reduces the amplitude to $1/e$ times its maximum value, then the half-width of this pulse is $(\sqrt{\sigma})/\pi$.

At later times, $t > 0$, we have to integrate (14) as it stands. To do this we require a detailed knowledge of n as a function of k. If we expand according to Taylor's theorem, we can write

$$n = n_0 + a(k - k_0) + \beta(k - k_0)^2/2 + \ldots$$

where

$$a = (dn/dk)_0 , \ \beta = (d^2n/dk^2)_0, \ldots \quad . \quad (19)$$

As a rule the first two terms are the most important, and if we neglect succeeding terms, we may integrate, using (17). The result is

$$\phi(x, t) = \int_{-\infty}^{+\infty} A \, e^{-\sigma(k - k_0)^2} e^{2\pi i\{kx - t(n_0 + a(k - k_0))\}} dk$$

$$= A \sqrt{\frac{\pi}{\sigma}} \, e^{-\pi^2(x - at)^2/\sigma} \cdot e^{2\pi i(k_0 x - n_0 t)}. \quad . \quad (20)$$

When $t = 0$, it is seen that this does reduce to (18), thus providing a check upon our calculations. The last term in (20) shows that the individual waves move with a wave velocity n_0/k_0, but their boundary amplitude is given by the first part of the expression, viz. $A \sqrt{\frac{\pi}{\sigma}} e^{-\pi^2(x - at)^2/\sigma}$.

Now this expression is exactly the same as in (18), drawn in fig. 26, except that it is displaced a distance at to the right. We conclude, therefore, that the group *as a whole* moves with velocity $a = (dn/dk)_0$, but that individual waves within the group have the wave velocity n_0/k_0. The velocity of the group as a whole is just what we have previously called the group velocity (7).

If we take one more term in (19) and integrate to obtain $\phi(x, t)$ we find that ϕ has the same form as in (20) except that σ is replaced by $\sigma + \pi\beta it$. The effect of this is twofold; in the first place it introduces a variable phase into the term $e^{2\pi i(k_0 x - n_0 t)}$, and in the second place it changes the exponential term in the boundary amplitude curve to the form

$$\exp \frac{-\pi^2 \sigma (x - at)^2}{\sigma^2 + \pi^2 \beta^2 t^2}.$$

This is still a Gaussian curve, but its half-width is increased to

$$\{(\sigma^2 + \pi^2 \beta^2 t^2)/\sigma\pi^2\}^{1/2}. \qquad . \qquad . \qquad . \quad (21)$$

We notice therefore that the wave packet moves with the wave velocity n_0/k_0, and group velocity $(dn/dk)_0$, spreading out as it goes in such a way that its half-width at time t is given by (21).

The importance of the group velocity lies mainly in the fact that in most problems where dispersion occurs, the group velocity is the velocity with which the energy is propagated. We have already met this in previous paragraphs.

§ 85. We shall next give a general discussion of the standard equation of wave motion $\nabla^2 \phi = \dfrac{1}{c^2} \dfrac{\partial^2 \phi}{\partial t^2}$, in which c is constant. We shall show that the value of ϕ at any point P (which may, without loss of generality be taken to be the origin) may be obtained from a knowledge of the values of ϕ, $\dfrac{\partial \phi}{\partial n}$ and $\dfrac{\partial \phi}{\partial t}$ on any given closed surface S, which may or may not surround P; the values of ϕ and its derivatives on S have to be associated with times which differ somewhat from the time at which we wish to determine ϕ_P.

Let us analyse ϕ into components with different frequencies; each component itself must satisfy the equation of wave motion, and by the principle of superposition, which holds when c is constant, we can add the various components together to obtain the full solution. Let us consider first that part of ϕ which is of frequency p; we may write it in the form

$$\psi(x, y, z)\, e^{ikct}, \qquad . \qquad . \qquad . \qquad (22)$$

where
$$k = 2\pi p/c. \qquad . \qquad . \qquad . \qquad (23)$$

ψ is the space part of the disturbance, and it satisfies the Poisson equation

$$(\nabla^2 + k^2)\psi = 0. \qquad . \qquad . \qquad (24)$$

This last equation may be solved by using Green's theorem.* This theorem states that if ψ_1 and ψ_2 are any two functions, and S is any closed surface, which may consist of two or more parts, such that ψ_1 and ψ_2 have no singularities inside it, then

$$\int \{\psi_2 \nabla^2 \psi_1 - \psi_1 \nabla^2 \psi_2\} d\tau = \int \left\{ \psi_2 \frac{\partial \psi_1}{\partial n} - \psi_1 \frac{\partial \psi_2}{\partial n} \right\} dS . \qquad (25)$$

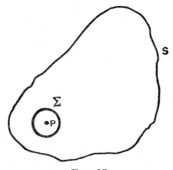

Fig. 27

The volume integral on the left-hand side is taken over

* See Rutherford, p. 65, equation (29).

the whole volume bounded by S, and $\partial/\partial n$ denotes differentiation along the outward normal to dS.

In this equation ψ_1 and ψ_2 are arbitrary, so we may put ψ_1 equal to ψ, the solution of (24), and $\psi_2 = \dfrac{e^{-ikr}}{r}$, r being measured radially from the origin P. We take the volume through which we integrate to be the whole volume contained between the given closed surface S (fig. 27) and a small sphere Σ around the origin. We have to exclude the origin because ψ_2 becomes infinite at that point. Fig. 27 is drawn for the case of P within S; the analysis holds just as well if P lies outside S.

Now it can easily be verified that $\nabla^2\psi_2 = -k^2\psi_2$, so that the left-hand side of (25) becomes $\int \psi_2(\nabla^2+k^2)\psi\,d\tau$, and this vanishes, since $(\nabla^2+k^2)\psi = 0$ by (24). The right-hand side of (25) consists of two parts, representing integrations over S and Σ. On Σ the outward normal is directed towards P and hence this part of the full expression is

$$\int \left\{ \frac{e^{-ikr}}{r}\left(-\frac{\partial\psi}{\partial r} \right) - \psi\left(-\frac{\partial}{\partial r}\left[\frac{e^{-ikr}}{r} \right] \right) \right\} d\Sigma.$$

When we make the radius of Σ tend to 0, only one term remains; it is

$$-\int \psi \frac{e^{-ikr}}{r^2}\,d\Sigma = -\int \psi \frac{e^{-ikr}}{r^2}\, . \, r^2 d\omega,$$

where $d\omega$ is an element of solid angle round P. Taking the limit as r tends to zero, this gives us a contribution $-4\pi\psi_P$. Equation (25) may therefore be written

$$4\pi\psi_P = \int \left\{ \frac{e^{-ikr}}{r}\frac{\partial\psi}{\partial n} - \psi\frac{\partial}{\partial n}\left(\frac{e^{-ikr}}{r} \right) \right\} dS$$

$$= \int \left\{ \frac{e^{-ikr}}{r}\frac{\partial\psi}{\partial n} - \psi\, e^{-ikr}\,\frac{\partial}{\partial n}\left(\frac{1}{r} \right) + ik\psi\frac{e^{-ikr}}{r}\frac{\partial r}{\partial n} \right\} dS.$$

Since by definition $\phi = \psi(xyz)e^{ikct}$, we can write this last equation in the form

$$\phi_P = \frac{1}{4\pi} \int X \, dS \qquad . \qquad . \qquad . \qquad (26)$$

where

$$X = \frac{e^{ik(ct-r)}}{r} \frac{\partial \psi}{\partial n} - \psi e^{ik(ct-r)} \frac{\partial}{\partial n}\left(\frac{1}{r}\right) + ik \, \psi \, \frac{e^{ik(ct-r)}}{r} \frac{\partial r}{\partial n},$$
$$= A - B + C, \text{ say.}$$

We may rewrite X in a simpler form; for on account of the time variation of ϕ, $\psi \, e^{ik(ct-r)}$ is the same as ϕ, taken, not at time t, but at time $t-r/c$. If we write this symbolically $[\phi]_{t-r/c}$, then $B = \frac{\partial}{\partial n}\left(\frac{1}{r}\right)[\phi]_{t-r/c}$. In a similar way, $A = \frac{1}{r}\left[\frac{\partial \phi}{\partial n}\right]_{t-r/c}$, and $C = \frac{1}{cr} \frac{\partial r}{\partial n}\left[\frac{\partial \phi}{\partial t}\right]_{t-r/c}$, where, for example, $\left[\frac{\partial \phi}{\partial n}\right]_{t-r/c}$ means that we evaluate $\partial\phi/\partial n$ as a function of x, y, z, t and *then* replace t by $t-r/c$. We call $t-r/c$ the **retarded time**. We have therefore proved that

$$\phi_P = \frac{1}{4\pi} \int X \, dS, \quad \text{where}$$

$$X = \frac{1}{r}\left[\frac{\partial \phi}{\partial n}\right]_{t-r/c} - \frac{\partial}{\partial n}\left(\frac{1}{r}\right)[\phi]_{t-r/c} + \frac{1}{cr} \frac{\partial r}{\partial n}\left[\frac{\partial \phi}{\partial t}\right]_{t-r/c}. \quad (27)$$

So far we have been dealing with waves of one definite frequency. But there is nothing in (27) which depends upon the frequency, and hence, by summation over all the components for each frequency present in our complete wave, we obtain a result exactly the same as (27) but without the restriction to a single frequency.

This theorem, which is due to Kirchhoff, is of great theoretical importance; for it implies (a) that the value of ϕ may be regarded as the sum of contributions $X/4\pi$ from each element of area of S; this may be called the law of addition of small elements, and is familiar in a law of addition of small elements, and is familiar in a slightly different form in optics as Huygens' Principle; and (b) that the contribution of dS depends on the value of ϕ, not at time t, but at time $t-r/c$. Now r/c is the time that a signal would take to get from dS to the point P, so that the contribution made by dS depends not on the present value of ϕ at dS, but on its value at that particular previous moment when it was necessary for a signal to leave dS in order that it should just have arrived at P. This is the justification for the title of retarded time, and for this reason also, $[\phi]_{t-r/c}$ is sometimes known as a **retarded potential**.

It is not difficult to verify that we could have obtained a solution exactly similar to the above, but involving $t+r/c$ instead of $t-r/c$; we should have taken ψ_2 in the previous work to be $\dfrac{e^{+ikr}}{r}$ instead of $\dfrac{e^{-ikr}}{r}$. In this way we should have obtained **advanced potentials**, $[\phi]_{t+r/c}$, and **advanced times**, instead of retarded potentials and retarded times. More generally, too, we could have superposed the two types of solution, but we shall not discuss this matter further.

In the case in which $c = \infty$, so that signals have an infinite velocity, the fundamental equation reduces to Laplace's equation,* $\nabla^2\phi = 0$, and the question of time variation does not arise. Our equation (27) reduces to the standard solution for problems of electrostatics.

§ 86. We shall apply this theory to the case of a source O sending out spherical harmonic waves, and we shall take S to be a closed surface surrounding the point P at which we want to calculate ϕ, as shown in fig. 28. Consider a small element of dS at Q; the outward normal makes angles θ_1 and θ with QO and PQ, and these two distances are r_1 and r. The value of ϕ at Q is given by the form appropriate to a spherical wave (see Chapter I,

* See Rutherford, p. 67, equation (33).

equation (24)) :

$$\phi_Q = \frac{a}{r_1} \cos m(ct - r_1) \qquad . \qquad , \qquad (28)$$

Thus

$$\frac{\partial \phi}{\partial n} = - \cos \theta_1 \frac{\partial \phi}{\partial r_1}$$

$$= a \cos \theta_1 \left\{ \frac{1}{r_1^2} \cos m(ct - r_1) - \frac{m}{r_1} \sin m(ct - r_1) \right\}.$$

Now $\lambda = 2\pi/m$, so that if r_1 is much greater than λ, which

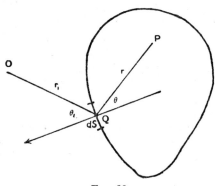

Fig. 28

will almost always happen in practical problems, we may put

$$\frac{\partial \phi}{\partial n} = - \frac{ma \cos \theta_1}{r_1} \sin m(ct - r_1).$$

Also

$$\frac{\partial}{\partial n}\left(\frac{1}{r}\right) = - \frac{1}{r^2} \cos \theta$$

and

$$\frac{\partial \phi}{\partial t} = - \frac{amc}{r_1} \sin m(ct - r_1).$$

The retarded values are easily found, and in fact, from (27),

$$X = - \frac{ma \cos \theta_1}{rr_1} \sin m(ct - [r + r_1])$$

$$+ \frac{a}{r^2 r_1} \cos \theta \cos m(ct - [r + r_1]) - \frac{1}{cr} \frac{amc}{r_1} \cos \theta \sin m(ct - [r + r_1]).$$

We may neglect the second term on the right if r_1 is much greater than λ, and so

$$X = -\frac{ma}{rr_1}(\cos\theta+\cos\theta_1)\sin m(ct-[r+r_1]) \quad . \quad (29)$$

Combining (29) with (26) it follows that

$$\phi_P = -\frac{1}{4\pi}\int \frac{ma}{rr_1}(\cos\theta + \cos\theta_1)\sin m(ct-[r+r_1])dS$$

$$= -\frac{a}{2\lambda}\int \frac{1}{rr_1}(\cos\theta + \cos\theta_1)\sin m(ct-[r+r_1])dS \ . \quad (30)$$

If, instead of a spherical wave, we had had a plane wave coming from the direction of O, we should write

$$\phi_Q = a\cos m(ct-r_1),$$

r_1 now being measured from some plane perpendicular to OQ, and (30) would be changed to

$$\phi_P = -\frac{a}{2\lambda}\int \frac{1}{r}(\cos\theta + \cos\theta_1)\sin m(ct-[r+r_1])dS. \quad (31)$$

We may interpret (30) and (31) as follows. The effect at P is the same as if each element dS sends out a wave of amplitude $\dfrac{A}{\lambda r}\left(\dfrac{\cos\theta+\cos\theta_1}{2}\right)dS$, A being the amplitude of the incident wave at dS; further, these waves are a quarter of a period in advance of the incident wave, as is shown by the term $-\sin m(ct-[r+r_1])$ instead of $\cos m(ct-r_1)$. $\frac{1}{2}(\cos\theta+\cos\theta_1)$ is called the **inclination factor** and if, as often happens, only small values of θ and θ_1 occur significantly, it has the value unity. This interpretation of (30) and (31) is known as **Fresnel's principle**.

The presence of this inclination factor removes a difficulty which was inherent in Huygens' principle ; this principle is usually stated in the form that each element of a wave-front emits wavelets in all directions, and these combine to form the observed progressive wave-front. In such a statement there is nothing to show why the wave does not progress backwards as well as forwards, since the wavelets should combine equally in either direction. The explanation is, of course, that for points behind the wave-front $\cos \theta$ is negative with a value either exactly or approximately equal to $-\cos \theta_1$, and so the inclination factor is small. Each wavelet is therefore propagated almost entirely in the forward direction.

Now let us suppose that some screens are introduced, and that they cover part of the surface of S. If we assume that the distribution of ϕ at any point Q near the screens is the same as it would have been if the screens were not present, we have merely to integrate (30) or (31) over those parts of S which are not covered. This approximation, which is known as **St Venant's principle**, is not rigorously correct, for there will be distortions in the value of ϕ_Q extending over several wavelengths from the edges of each screen. It is, however, an excellent approximation for most optical problems, where λ is small; indeed (30) and (31) form the basis of the whole theory of the diffraction of light. With sound waves, on the other hand, in which λ is often of the same order of magnitude as the size of the screen, it is only roughly correct.

§ 87. Let us illustrate this discussion with an example of the analysis summarised in (31). Consider an infinite screen (fig. 29) which we may take to be the xy plane. A small part of this screen (large compared with the wavelength of the waves but small compared with other distances involved) is cut away, leaving a hole through which waves may pass. We suppose that a set of plane harmonic waves is travelling in the positive z direction, and falls on the screen; we want to find the resulting disturbance at a point P behind the screen.

K

In accordance with § 86 we take the surface S to be the infinite xy plane, completed by the infinite hemisphere on the positive side of the xy plane. We may divide the

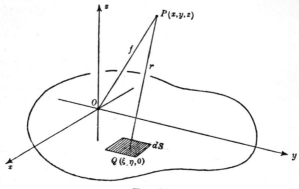

FIG. 29

contributions to (31) into three parts. The first part arises from the aperture, the second part arises from the rest of the screen, and the third part arises from the hemisphere.

If the incident harmonic waves are represented by $\phi = a \cos m(ct-z)$ this first contribution amounts to

$$ -\frac{a}{2\lambda}\int \frac{1}{r}\,(1+\cos\theta)\sin m(ct-r)dS. $$

We have put $\theta_1 = 0$ in this expression since the waves fall normally on to the xy plane. We shall only be concerned here with points P which lie behind, or nearly behind, the aperture, so that we may also put $\cos\theta = 1$ without loss of accuracy. This contribution is then

$$ -\frac{a}{\lambda}\int \frac{1}{r}\sin m(ct-r)dS \qquad . \qquad . \qquad (32) $$

The second part, which comes from the remainder of the xy plane, vanishes, since no waves penetrate the screen and thus there are no secondary waves starting there.

The third part, from the infinite hemisphere, also vanishes, because the only waves that can reach this part of S are those that came from the aperture, and when these waves reach the hemisphere their inclination factor is zero. Thus (32) is in actual fact the only non-zero contribution and we may write

$$\phi_P = -\frac{a}{\lambda}\int \frac{1}{r} \sin m(ct-r)dS \quad . \quad . \quad (33)$$

Let P be the point (x, y, z) and consider the contribution to (33) that arises from a small element of the aperture at Q $(\xi, \eta, 0)$. If $OP = f$, and $QP = r$, we have

$$\begin{aligned} f^2 &= x^2+y^2+z^2, \\ r^2 &= (x-\xi)^2+(y-\eta)^2+z^2 \\ &= f^2-2x\xi-2y\eta+\xi^2+\eta^2 \quad . \quad . \quad (34) \end{aligned}$$

Let us make the assumption that the aperture is so small that ξ^2/f^2 and η^2/f^2 may be neglected. Then to this approximation (34) shows us that

$$r = f - \frac{x\xi+y\eta}{f}.$$

So

$$\phi_P = -\frac{a}{\lambda}\int \frac{1}{r} \sin m\left(ct-f+\frac{x\xi+y\eta}{f}\right)dS.$$

Again without loss of accuracy, to the approximation to which we are working, we may put $1/r = 1/f$, and then we obtain

$$\phi_P = -A \sin \{m(ct-f)+\epsilon\},$$

where

$$A^2 = C^2+S^2, \quad \tan \epsilon = S/C,$$

and

$$C(x, y) = \frac{a}{\lambda f} \int \cos \frac{2\pi}{\lambda f} (x\xi + y\eta) d\xi d\eta,$$

$$S(x, y) = \frac{a}{\lambda f} \int \sin \frac{2\pi}{\lambda f} (x\xi + y\eta) d\xi d\eta \quad . \quad . \quad (35)$$

Once we know the shape of the aperture it is an easy matter to evaluate these integrals. Thus, if we consider the case of a rectangular aperture bounded by the lines $\xi = \pm a$, $\eta = \pm \beta$, we soon verify that $S = 0$, and that

$$C = \frac{a}{\lambda f} \int_{-a}^{+a} \int_{-\beta}^{+\beta} \cos \frac{2\pi}{\lambda f} (x\xi + y\eta) d\eta \, d\xi$$

$$= \frac{4a}{\lambda f} \frac{\sin pax}{px} \frac{\sin p\beta y}{py}, \quad . \quad . \quad . \quad (36)$$

where $p = 2\pi/\lambda f$. If we are dealing with light waves, then the intensity is proportional to C^2 and the diffraction pattern thus observed in the plane $z = f$ consists of a grill network, with zero intensity corresponding to the values of x and y satisfying either $\sin pax = 0$, or $\sin p\beta y = 0$ but excluding $x = 0$ and $y = 0$.

§ 88. The discussion of the last paragraph related to the case of plane waves falling normally on an aperture whose size, while large compared with the wavelength, was still small compared with the distance from the aperture to the screen on which the pattern was being observed. We might refer to this as diffraction at a pin-hole. But the equations (35) arise in another far more important way which we must now explain, and which is known as **Fraunhofer Diffraction**.

Consider (fig. 30) a plane wave shown as AA' in the diagram falling normally on a convergent lens L. (L replaces the previous pin-hole.) This lens will convert the plane wave into a spherical wave which converges at Z, the focus. On account of the finite size of the lens the focus is not perfect, and we ask the question : what will be the intensity observed at a point P in the focal plane through Z ?

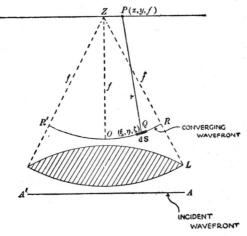

Fig. 30

To answer this question it is convenient to draw the wavefront ROR' of a wave that has just left the lens. We may regard this as part of a spherical surface with centre Z and radius equal to the focal length f. If we take O as origin and OZ as axis of Z, then the coordinates (ξ, η, ζ) of any point Q on the surface satisfy the equation

$$\xi^2+\eta^2+(\zeta-f)^2 = f^2,$$

i.e. $$\xi^2+\eta^2+\zeta^2 = 2f\zeta \qquad . \qquad . \qquad . \quad (37)$$

Now by reasoning very similar to that used in § **87** we may argue that if P is near Z, the total effect at P is just the sum of separate contributions arising from all the elements dS within the curved wavefront RR'. Let us suppose that the inclination factor (p. 144) may be put equal to unity, and that the amplitude at all points on RR' is a; this is the same as the amplitude in the incident wave AA'. Thus

$$\phi_Q = a \cos m(ct+f) \qquad . \qquad . \qquad . \quad (38)$$

Let us write (x, y, f) for the coordinates of the point P at which the observation is made, and put $QP = r$. Then the appropriate form of (30) is

$$\phi_P = -\frac{a}{\lambda} \int \frac{1}{r} \sin m(ct-r+f)\, dS \quad . \qquad . \quad (39)$$

We may replace $1/r$ by $1/f$ in the first part of this integral: and note that

$$r^2 = (x-\xi)^2+(y-\eta)^2+(f-\zeta)^2$$
$$= f^2+x^2+y^2-2x\xi-2y\eta \qquad \text{by (37)}.$$

In cases where this type of diffraction is important, f is large and x and y are small. We may therefore write

$$r^2 = f^2-2x\xi-2y\eta,$$

so that effectively

$$r = f-\frac{x\xi+y\eta}{f} \quad . \qquad . \qquad . \qquad . \quad (40)$$

Combining (39) and (40) we have

$$\phi_P = -\frac{a}{\lambda f} \int \sin m\left(ct+\frac{x\xi+y\eta}{f}\right) dS.$$

Thus, on integrating,

$$\phi_P = -A \sin(mct+\epsilon), \quad . \qquad . \qquad . \quad (41)$$

where A and ϵ are given by precisely the same formulæ as in (35).

This kind of analysis will apply particularly to the image of a star in a telescope of long focal length. The star is so far away that it may be regarded as giving out a beam of parallel light. We have just shown therefore that the image of the star is not a point, but a pattern with maxima and minima, depending on the shape and size of the lens. For example, if a rectangular aperture (bounded by $\xi = \pm a$, $\eta = \pm \beta$) is placed immediately behind the lens L, the diffraction pattern is a grill network, as in (36). And a circular aperture (question 9 at the end of the chapter) gives diffraction rings around Z. In any case the finite extent of the central maximum, or zone, will put limits to our power of resolving the light from two close stars. For if the geometrical images of the two stars lie within one another's central zones, we shall experience difficulty in distinguishing whether there is really only one star, or two. But there is no space here to deal with this important matter any more closely.

§ 89. We conclude this chapter with a discussion of the equation

$$\nabla^2 \phi = \frac{1}{c^2} \frac{\partial^2 \phi}{\partial t^2} - 4\pi\rho, \qquad . \qquad . \qquad (42)$$

where ρ is some given function of x, y, z and t. When $\rho = 0$ this is the standard equation of wave motion, whose solution was discussed in § 85. Equation (42) has already occurred in the propagation of electric waves when charges were present (Chapter VIII, equations (17′) and (18′)). We may solve this equation in a manner very similar to that used in § 85. Thus, suppose that $\rho(x, y, z, t)$ is expressed in the form of a Fourier series with respect to t, viz.,

$$\rho(x, y, z, t) = \sum_k a_k(x, y, z)e^{ikct} \qquad . \qquad . \qquad (43)$$

There may be a finite, or an infinite, number of different values of k, and instead of a summation over discrete values of k we could, if we desired, include also an integration over a continuous range of values. We shall discuss here the case of discrete values of k; the student will easily adapt our method of solution to deal with a continuum.

Suppose that $\phi(x, y, z, t)$ is itself analysed into components similar to (43), and let us write, similarly to (22),

$$\phi(x, y, z, t) = \sum_k \psi_k(x, y, z)e^{ikct} \qquad . \qquad . \qquad (44)$$

the values of k being the same as in (43). If we substitute (43) and (44) into (42), and then equate coefficients of e^{ikct}, we obtain an equation for ψ_k. It is

$$(\nabla^2 + k^2)\psi_k = -4\pi a_k \qquad . \qquad . \qquad (45)$$

This equation may be solved just as in § 85. Using Green's theorem as in (25), we put $\psi_1 = \psi_k(x, y, z)$, $\psi_2 = \dfrac{e^{-ikr}}{r}$, taking Σ and S to be the same as in fig. 27. With these values, it is easily seen that the left-hand side of (25) no longer vanishes, but has the value

$$-4\pi \int \frac{a_k(x, y, z)}{r} e^{-ikr} d\tau, \quad . \qquad . \qquad (46)$$

the integral being taken over the space between Σ and S. The right-hand side may be treated exactly as in § 85, and gives two terms, one due to integration over Σ, and the other to integration over S. The first of these is

$$-4\pi \psi_k(x_P, y_P, z_P) \qquad . \qquad . \qquad (47)$$

The second may be calculated just as on p. 140. Gathering the various terms together, we obtain

$$\psi_k(x_P, y_P, z_P) = \int \frac{a_k(x, y, z)}{r} e^{-ikr} d\tau$$

$$+ \frac{1}{4\pi} \int \left\{ \frac{e^{-ikr}}{r} \frac{\partial \psi_k}{\partial n} - \psi_k e^{-ikr} \frac{\partial}{\partial n}\left(\frac{1}{r}\right) + ik \psi_k \frac{e^{-ikr}}{r} \frac{\partial r}{\partial n} \right\} dS \quad . \quad (48)$$

Combining (43), (44) and (48) we can soon verify that our solution can be written in the form

$$\phi(x_P, y_P, z_P) = \int \frac{[\rho]_{t-r/c}}{r} d\tau + \frac{1}{4\pi} \int X \, dS, \quad . \quad (49)$$

where X is defined by (27). This solution reduces to (27) in the case where $\rho = 0$, while it reduces to the well-known solution of electrostatics in the case where $c = \infty$.

We have now obtained the required solution of (42). Often, however, there will be conditions imposed by the physical nature of our problem that allow us to simplify (49). Thus, if $\rho(x, y, z, t)$ is finite in extent, and has only had non-zero values for a finite time $t > t_0$, we can make $X = 0$ by taking S to be the sphere at infinity. This follows because X is measured at the retarded time $t - r/c$, and if r is large enough, we shall have $t - r/c < t_0$, so that $[\phi]_{t-r/c}$ and its derivatives will be identically zero on S. In such a case we have the simple result

$$\phi(x_P, y_P, z_P) = \int \frac{[\rho]_{t-r/c}}{r} d\tau, \quad . \quad . \quad (50)$$

the integration being taken over the whole of space. Retarded potentials calculated in this way are very important in the Classical theory of electrons.

§ 89.   Examples

(1) An observer who is at rest notices that the frequency of a car appears to drop from 272 to 256 per second as the car passes him. Show that the speed of the car is approximately 23 m.p.h. How fast must he travel in the direction of the car for the apparent frequency to rise to 280 per second, and what would it drop to in that case ?

(2) Show that in the Doppler effect, when the source and observer are not moving in the same direction, the formulæ of § 80 are valid to give the various changes in frequency, provided that u and v denote, not the actual velocities, but the components of the two velocities along the direction in which the waves reach the observer.

(3) The amplitude A of a harmonic wave $A \cos 2\pi(nt-kx)$ is modulated so that $A = a+b \cos 2\pi pt+c \cos^2 2\pi pt$. Show that combination tones of frequencies $n\pm p$, $n\pm 2p$ appear, and calculate their partial amplitudes.

(4) The dielectric constant of a certain gas varies with the wavelength according to the law $\epsilon = A+B/\lambda^2-C\lambda^2$, where A, B and C are constants. Show that the group velocity U of electromagnetic waves is given in terms of the wave velocity V by the formula

$$U = V \frac{A\ \ -2C\lambda^2}{A+\dfrac{B}{\lambda^2}-C\lambda^2}.$$

(5) In a region of anomalous dispersion (§ 83) the dielectric constant obeys the approximate law $\epsilon = 1+\dfrac{A\lambda^2}{\lambda^2-\lambda_0^2}$. A more accurate expression is $\epsilon = 1+\dfrac{A\lambda^2(\lambda^2-\lambda_0^2)}{(\lambda^2-\lambda_0^2)^2+B\lambda^2}$, where A, B and λ_0 are constants. Find the group velocity of electric waves in these two cases.

(6) Calculate the group velocity for ripples on an infinitely deep lake. (§ 54, equation (54).)

(7) Investigate the motion of a wavepacket (§ 84) for which the amplitude a is given in terms of the wave number k by the relation

$$a(k) = 1 \text{ if } |k-k_0|<k_1$$
$$= 0 \text{ otherwise,}$$

k_0 and k_1 being constants. Assume that only the first two terms of the Taylor expansion of n in terms of k are required. Show that at time t the disturbance is

$$\phi(x,\ t) = \frac{\sin\ \{2\pi(x-at)k_1\}}{\pi(x-at)}\ e^{2\pi i(k_0 x-n_0 t)},$$

where $a = (dn/dk)_0$. Verify that the wavepacket moves as a whole with the velocity a.

(8) Show that when dS is normal to the incident light (§ 86), the inclination factor is $\dfrac{1+\cos\ \theta}{2}$. Plot this function against θ, and thus show that each little element dS of a

wave gives zero amplitude immediately behind the direction of wave motion. Using the fact that the energy is proportional to the square of the amplitude of ϕ, show that, taken alone, each small element sends out 7/8 of its energy forwards in front of the wave, and only 1/8 backwards.

(9) A plane wave falls normally on a small circular aperture of radius b. Discuss the pattern observed at a large distance f behind the aperture. Show that with the formulæ of § 87, if the incident wave is $\phi = a \cos m(ct-z)$, then $S = 0$, and if P is the point $(x, 0, f)$, then

$$C = \frac{2a}{\lambda f} \int_{-b}^{+b} \sqrt{(b^2 - \xi^2)} \, . \, \cos p\xi \, d\xi \text{ where } p = 2\pi x/\lambda f,$$

$$= \frac{4ab^2}{\lambda f} \int_0^{\pi/2} \cos (pb \cos \theta) \sin^2\theta \, d\theta.$$

Expand $\cos (pb \cos \theta)$ in a power series in $\cos \theta$, and hence show that

$$C = \frac{\pi ab^2}{\lambda f} \left\{ 1 - \frac{1}{2} \left(\frac{k}{1!} \right)^2 + \frac{1}{3} \left(\frac{k^2}{2!} \right)^2 - \frac{1}{4} \left(\frac{k^3}{3!} \right)^2 + \ldots \right\},$$

where $k = pb/2 = \pi bx/\lambda f$. Since the system is symmetrical around the z axis, this gives the disturbance at any point in the plane $z = f$. It can be shown that the infinite series is in fact a Bessel function of order unity. It gives rise to diffraction rings of diminishing intensity for large values of x.

(10) The total charge q on a conducting sphere of radius a is made to vary so that $q = 4\pi a^2\sigma$, where $\sigma = 0$ for $t < 0$, and $\sigma = \sigma_0 \sin pt$ for $t > 0$. Show that if $\epsilon = \mu = 1$, (§70 eq. (18')) the electric potential ϕ at a distance R from the centre of the sphere is given by

$$ct < R - a, \qquad \phi = 0,$$

$$R - a < ct < R + a, \qquad \phi = \frac{2\pi ac\sigma_0}{pR} \left\{ 1 - \cos p \left(t - \frac{R-a}{c} \right) \right\},$$

$$R + a < ct, \qquad \phi = \frac{4\pi ac\sigma_0}{pR} \sin \frac{pa}{c} \sin p \left(t - \frac{R}{c} \right).$$

(11) The wave represented by $\phi = A \cos 2\pi(nt - kx + \epsilon)$ suffers phase modulation in which $\epsilon = a + b \cos 2\pi pt$. a, b

and p are constants, and b^2 may be neglected. Show that in addition to the wave of given frequency n and amplitude A, combination tones appear, with frequency $n \pm p$, and amplitude $\pi A b$.

(12) The wave represented by $\phi = A \cos 2\pi(nt - kx + \epsilon)$ suffers frequency modulation in which $n = n_0 + a \cos 2\pi pt$. a, n_0 and p are constants, a^2 may be neglected and $p \ll n_0$. Show that in addition to a wave of frequency n_0 and amplitude A, there are four combination tones of frequency $n_0 \pm p \pm a$ and amplitude $\frac{1}{4}A$. It may be assumed that at is small.

$\Big[$ANSWERS: $1 . c/34$, where c = velocity of sound, 249 per second; $3. a + c/2, b/2, c/4$; $5. V\left\{1 - \dfrac{A \lambda_0^2 \lambda^2}{(\lambda^2 - \lambda_0^2)(\lambda^2 - \lambda_0^2 + A \lambda^2)}\right\}$,

$V\left\{1 + \dfrac{A \lambda^2 \{B \lambda^4 - \lambda_0^2(\lambda^2 - \lambda_0^2)^2\}}{\epsilon\{(\lambda^2 - \lambda_0^2)^2 + B \lambda^2\}^2}\right\}$, where V = wave velocity;

$6. U = \frac{1}{2}c + \dfrac{2\pi \mathsf{T}}{\lambda \rho c}.\Big]$

INDEX

The Numbers refer to pages

PRINTED IN GREAT BRITAIN BY OLIVER AND BOYD LTD., EDINBURGH